JESUS
OF NAZARETH

Joy Harington

JESU

Doubleday & Company, Inc., Garden City, New York

OF NAZARETH

FOR TESSA

LIBRARY OF CONGRESS CATALOG CARD NUMBER 57–11421

AUTHOR'S NOTE

It has been suggested that the readers of this book might like to hear something of how it came to be written.

When I see my name on the cover under the title *Jesus of Nazareth* I am filled with a sort of horror at my temerity and impudence in daring to set myself forward as a biographer of our Lord. And then I remember how it all began.

It was in the autumn of 1954 that Sir Ian Jacob, Director General of the B.B.C., invited each department of the Television Service to put forward ideas for what he called a special project. We were to imagine that we had a budget three or four times larger than the normal one for a programme and to say how we would use it. Needless to say imaginations ran wild. Television production is an expensive business and we never seem to have enough money.

I put in two suggestions. One was that we should take our film cameras to places in the world where important things had happened, for instance, the Holy Land, and bring to people's homes the places whose names are so familiar to young and old.

The second suggestion grew out of something that had been in my mind for a long time. Every year we put on a Nativity play at Christmas and sometimes a Passion play at Easter and it seemed to me that for many people Jesus was a baby in a manger or a figure on a Cross while the time in between, the life that our Lord lived during the three years of his Ministry, remained a disconnected collection of rather obscure stories. The second suggestion then was that we should do a series of plays on the life of Christ during the months between the events celebrated in the two great Christian festivals.

To my amazement, both these ideas were accepted as one by the Director General and I was told to go ahead and prepare a documentary life of Christ and to go to the Holy Land to film the outdoor scenes.

It was tremendously exciting and absolutely overwhelming. It is one thing to put forward an airy idealistic suggestion, and quite another to have it landed in your lap with the responsibility of making it a concrete reality. But the work began.

Anyone who has tried to write a 'harmony' of the Four Gospels will know, better than I did then, the seemingly insuperable difficulties that such an undertaking presents. And many were the discussions, the trials and the errors that went into the arrangement of eight dramatic episodes, each one of which must be complete in itself while the whole cycle must preserve the essential pattern and impact of the story. But at last we had a summary drawn up and the next question was the style of writing.

The programme was to be a living document of our Lord's life and teaching as told in the New Testament. The viewers were to see the things happening where they happened and hear the words spoken that they could read in their Bibles. Should then the story be told entirely in the words of the Gospel writers? Should the authorised, the revised, or a modern translation be used? How much invented dialogue would be permitted? It was our Religious Advisors who advocated that at all costs this presentation of the Gospel story must avoid what they called "the stained glass window" approach. It must be real, vigorous, and in the modern idiom.

It was hard to lay aside the beautiful and familiar cadences of the authorised version and strive to match a modern translation of Christ's words with invented dialogue from the other characters. One felt so completely inadequate. Perhaps it was this sense of inadequacy that made it possible to attempt the task at all. We all knew that what we had to do was to give our best. To strive with all the faith and skill and talent we could muster to make this a true and living document of our Lord's life and teaching. We knew that not even superhuman genius could succeed and none of us pretended to genius. We were artists and craftsmen, actors and technicians and we were going to attempt what artists and craftsmen had been striving to do for nearly two thousand years with the tools of their trade. We had before us the greatest of all stories and our tools were the complicated machinery of the Television Service.

I suppose a writer's greatest asset is imagination but because of the discipline imposed by the framework of the Gospel story it had in this case to be strictly curbed and directed. Imagination had to be used when creating background and building character. But whereas with almost any other adaptation one could invent and dispose scenes and characters, in this story there were not only the Four Gospels but the Christian Church and a wealth of scholarship to study and adhere to strictly.

I am not a Greek scholar but I searched around among the different translations and unscrupulously 'borrowed.' One very happy discovery was a translation of Jesus' words to Jairus' daughter which in the authorised version reads, 'Damsel, I say unto thee, arise.' Apparently this phrase in Aramaic was the common morning greeting. It was the phrase used to awaken people. In fact, it meant "it's time to get up." The two sentences "She is not dead but sleeping" followed almost at once by "little girl, it's time to get up" brought the scene very much to life and within our understanding.

Sometimes in the course of study a tradition would come to light which I would eagerly seize upon. For instance, the belief that the man with the withered hand who was healed on the Sabbath day was a stone mason and said to Jesus "Sir, I'm a stone mason. I make a living by my hands. I pray you heal me, Jesus. I am ashamed to beg." This and many other stories which have been handed down for generations perhaps almost from the days of the first written gospels helped immeasurably to build character and fill in the background. But still a certain amount had to be imagined and sometimes I felt that the script would never be written. They were read, re-read, checked, revised, rewritten time and time again and at last they were ready and casting and production plans began.

There were countless things that had to be decided and there were many problems but we resolved them as best we could as we went along. I think we were all aware all the time that we were attempting the impossible. That the story, or rather the truth, we were trying to interpret was so much greater than anything we could do to it. Far from making us disheartened this had the effect of making everyone work flat out. Every department, each individual, each actor gave of his very best and the result was that the eternal truth that we were trying to interpret outshone our efforts and came through our complicated machinery clear and shining.

The response from viewers was greater than anything we had dared to anticipate. Letters poured in from parents and children, teachers and clergymen, and all kinds of people, some of them lonely or bedridden, who had been helped by the programme. One of the remarks that pleased me most was told me by the mother of an eleven-year-old boy who, when the series was over, said, "Well, if I had lived in those days I'd have had to follow Jesus."

I hope that some of you who read this book may feel the same.

The photographs that illustrate this book are stills from a cycle of plays called "Jesus of Nazareth" which was transmitted by B.B.C. Television during Lent 1956. I would like to thank the B.B.C. for giving me the opportunity to write and produce those plays and this book.

Grateful thanks also to the Reverend Robert Walton who helped me so immeasurably with the preparation of the scripts, to Professor T. W. Manson who checked them, and lastly to our many friends in Jordan and Israel.

Since we took only one actor to the Holy Land; Tom Fleming who was to play the part of Jesus, it was necessary to enlist the aid of the local people in whatever town or village we found ourselves to be the disciples and crowds which formed such an essential part of our story.

I shall never cease to be grateful for the friendliness and enthusiasm with which the people of Jordan and Israel (few of them Christians) responded to our often extraordinary demands.

These included: All the boys of one village being given the day off from school to act for us because "Everywhere Jesus went he was followed by crowds." The entire population of another village turning out on a Moslem Feast Day to form the palm-waving crowds along the route of the Triumphant Entry into Jerusalem. A young Arab, at a moment's notice, putting on a tunic of camel's hair and spending an afternoon waist-deep in the river Jordan. Four Israeli fishermen cheerfully submitting to having false beards stuck on their chins and being stripped of their clothes, to cast their nets and row their boat up and down the Sea of Galilee as often as the hazards of filming required, and the gardeners and workmen of the Garden of Gethsemane who exchanged their spades and rakes for "torches and weapons" and one peaceful night marched through the olive trees of their garden to "arrest Jesus."

You will see many of these people in the photographs in this book and I am glad of this opportunity to thank them.

Joy Harington.
London, 1957.

CONTENTS
and Illustrations

PART I

The Boy Jesus

Nazareth was a small town built on the brow of a hill, a day's journey from Lake Galilee. As it was an inland town its people were not fishermen like the men of Capernaum and Bethsaida but for the most part craftsmen, tradesmen and farmers. Among the Galilee hills the shepherd led his sheep, the farmer sowed and reaped his harvest, and ploughed his land with a pair of oxen yoked together—and in the streets of Nazareth the children played in the hot sun.

To-day they were playing at funerals. First came the music maker, playing a mournful dirge on his reed-pipe, then the procession of mourners, the girls with veils over their faces and some of the boys dressed up in their fathers' coats, looking very serious. Suddenly one of the boys tickled another and they burst out laughing.

'No—no—no,' scolded the piper. 'You're supposed to be a funeral procession. What's the good of my playing a dirge if you laugh?'

'We can't help it, they look so funny,' giggled a little girl.

'Anyway,' said the smallest boy, 'I'm tired of playing funerals.'

'Let's play weddings,' said another boy. 'Come on, play us a wedding tune, a dance.'

'What's the use of my playing anything if you change the game in the middle? When I play a dirge you laugh, when I pipe a dance you'll probably cry.'

At this all the children burst out laughing and began to dance round the disgruntled piper singing 'I mourned to you and you did not weep—I piped to you and you did not dance,' until the piper cheered up and began to play a happier tune. One of the girls made a wreath of wild anemones for the 'bridegroom' and they had just begun their game when the rabbi came down the street. He stopped and waited for the children to give him the formal greeting he had taught them.

'Peace be unto you, rabbi,' they chanted, bowing low.

'Unto you also let there be peace,' replied the rabbi. 'Now, which of you boys are coming to Jerusalem for your first Passover this week?'

Two of the boys who were twelve years old put up their hands.

'Bless you, my sons. Remember all you have been taught and remember your manners so you may do credit to Nazareth. Peace be unto you.' And he walked on down the street.

'I say,' said one of the boys. 'I'd forgotten that we start for Jerusalem to-morrow. I must be off home and help make up the packs for the ass. Peace be unto you,' he called as he ran off home. The other twelve-year-old said that he too was expected home early, and waving good-bye to his friends he went into the carpenter's shop that was his home.

In the little room behind Joseph's carpenter's shop that served as both kitchen and living-room, Mary was busy with her baking. As she drew two of the loaves from the oven, she heard the familiar sound of Jesus' feet scuffling in the shavings.

'Is that you, Jesus?' called Mary.

'Yes, mother,' said the boy, running into the room. He stopped and sniffed appreciatively. 'What a lovely smell.'

'It's the bread baking for the journey to-morrow. These two loaves are done; put them in the pack for me, will you?'

Jesus took the round, flat loaves in his hands. 'Aren't they big?' he said. 'They were tiny this morning!'

Mary laughed. 'That's the yeast I put in the dough. A pinch of yeast will work away inside the dough and turn it into good bread.'

'How?' asked Jesus. 'How does it work inside?'

'I don't know,' said Mary, laughing. 'It must be a secret.'

Jesus picked up a pinch of yeast between finger and thumb. 'It doesn't look very powerful, does it?' he said. 'Fancy it making such a difference,' and he packed the two loaves into a saddle bag. 'Of course we'll be having *un*leavened bread at the Passover supper, won't we?'

'Yes,' said his mother. 'I'm taking flour to make that. These are just for the journey.'

'Does unleavened just mean without yeast?' asked Jesus.

'Yes, of course. You know the story. How when the children of Israel had to flee from Egypt they had no time to finish making their bread, so they took it unleavened, just as it was. That's why we have it at the Passover, remembering them. Here are the spices.'

Jesus packed them carefully into the corners of the bag. 'Are we taking the lamb for the feast, too?'

'No, we'll buy that in Jerusalem.'

'Mother,' said Jesus, suddenly remembering something, 'you know that sheep that the shepherd lost? Well, he's found it. I was playing on the hills with some of the boys and we met the shepherd coming down—carrying it over his shoulder.'

'Oh, I *am* glad,' said Mary.

'So was he,' said Jesus. 'He was whistling away as he came down the hill and he called out to us, "Rejoice with me, boys—I have found my lost sheep."'

Mary laughed. 'I expect he'll make more fuss of that sheep for a while than of all the rest of his flock put together.' She handed him the dried fruit she had been wrapping. 'What else did you do to-day?'

'We looked for birds' nests and saw lots of them. A sparrow had fallen out of one and we put it back. And, do you know, we actually saw a fox? It was just creeping into its hole in a bank—oh, and mother, there are lots of wild anemones in the fields: pink and red and a sort of royal purple.'

'And why,' asked his mother, chaffing him, 'didn't you bring me some?'

'I did pick some,' said Jesus, 'but we used them when we were playing weddings and I'm afraid they're dead now. Isn't it a pity they die so soon?'

He went on packing the bag until everything was safely stored in it, and he had just strapped it up when Joseph came in and announced that the sky was red, so they could expect a fine day for to-morrow.

'If that bag's ready I'll put it with the tent and blankets ready to strap on the ass in the morning,' he added.

'Shall we be sleeping out?' asked Jesus eagerly.

'Yes,' said Joseph, smiling at the boy, 'it's four days' journey to Jerusalem and the inns will be packed with the foreign pilgrims.'

'Oh, it's much better to sleep in a tent.'

Mary said she thought Jesus had better have his supper at once so that he could get to bed early. Joseph cut some of the new bread for him, while Mary brought him some fruit.

'I can hardly believe I'm going to Jerusalem at last,' said Jesus.

'At last!' echoed Joseph. 'Did the twelve years go so slowly?'

'No, but every year when I've seen you and mother go, and all the other people from Nazareth, I've longed and longed for the time when I could go with you to see the Holy City and the temple.'

'You've been in the temple once before, you know.'

'But I don't remember it.'

'No, you were only a baby,' said Joseph, 'but it was a great day for your mother and me. There was an old man called Simeon in the temple that day and he took you in his arms and blessed you.'

'What did he say?'

Joseph hesitated. It was Mary who answered. 'He said that you would grow up to be "a light to the Gentiles and the glory of God's people, Israel."'

Jesus did not speak for a moment, but thought this over while he went on eating his supper. He took another piece of bread before he spoke, the words coming slowly.

'The Gentiles are God's people, too. When I'm a man. . . .' He turned to Joseph. 'I am almost a man, aren't I?'

'So says our law,' said Joseph. 'Now you begin to put aside childish things and train for your manhood.'

'Yes,' said Jesus, and he told Joseph how the rabbi had explained that after this Passover he would be ready to learn a trade. Most of the boys were learning their fathers' trades—he'd be a carpenter, he said, and help Joseph in the shop. Joseph and Mary exchanged glances, both thinking of how indeed he would be called to do his Father's work.

Jesus went on with his supper, and Mary told him of his cousin, John, whom he would meet in Jerusalem. 'He's a fine boy,' she said, 'big and strong and fearless. A great blessing to cousin Elizabeth and Zacharias who are old.'

'What work is he learning to do?' asked Jesus. 'Cousin Zacharias is a priest, isn't he? Will John be a priest, too?'

'A priest?' said Mary. 'He may be a priest, Jesus, but whatever work he does he will be God's messenger.'

'Messenger?'

'He will prepare the way. Prepare the people of Israel for their Messiah.'

'You mean, God has chosen him to be a prophet, like Elijah or Elisha?'

His mother nodded.

'The messenger the scriptures speak of, "Behold I will send my messenger before thy face to prepare the way"?' Mary nodded again. 'Mother!'

'Go to bed now, my son,' urged Mary, and Jesus threw his arms round her, then turned to Joseph, who kissed his forehead and said, 'The Lord bless you and keep you; the Lord make His face to shine upon you and give you His peace.'

Jesus went to the shelf to get his sleeping mat, which he spread in the alcove, while Mary took a little lamp and put it near him, pausing while he said his evening prayer: 'Father, into Thy hands I commend my spirit.' Then as his mother bent to tuck the blanket round him he said happily, 'Mother, won't it be exciting sleeping in a tent?'

Mary laughed as she tucked him up, and left him to sleep.

Next morning the streets of Nazareth were filled with bustle. Men and boys and sometimes whole families came from the houses to begin the yearly pilgrimage to the Holy City. To the door of his carpenter's shop Joseph led his ass, and soon Mary and Jesus came out and they all set off together, leading the ass laden with all they would need on their long journey. Jesus' playfellows waved them good-bye and shouted farewells.

On they went all that day, setting up their tent at nightfall, exchanging friendly words with neighbours camping near them, and with strangers who were following the same road to Jerusalem.

On the third night they were near Jericho, and Joseph and Jesus pitched their tent near another in front of which a woman was stirring a pot over a fire. Mary had been to the nearby well to fill a pitcher with water, and as she passed the woman called a greeting, and asked how far she had travelled.

'From Nazareth,' said Mary; 'three days' journey.'

Jesus was kindling a fire with dried grass. 'It's a different grass here in Jericho—isn't it pretty?' he said to his mother as he thrust a bundle into the flame. The fire blazed up, and the man from the neighbouring tent offered them wood for it, which Jesus accepted with gratitude. Their new friend warned them that there were bandits in the hills between Jericho and Jerusalem, and the two families agreed to travel together for safety. Suddenly a boy from a nearby tent ran over to them as they sat by their fire and told them that the Roman soldiers were searching the tents and baggage for weapons.

'I wish I had one,' he said to Jesus. 'I'd like to fight against them and drive them out of our country.'

Presently a centurion and two soldiers appeared. Anxiously Joseph asked what had happened.

'Just a routine inspection,' replied the centurion.

Jesus showed the soldier their tent and baggage while the centurion questioned Joseph.

'Where are you from?'

'From Nazareth in Galilee.'

'Galilee, eh? That's a place that's given us some trouble in the last year or two. What is your trade?'

'A carpenter.'

'Is there anyone in Jerusalem who could vouch for you?'

'My wife's cousin comes from Judea. Her husband is a priest and well respected in the temple.'

'What is his name?'

'Zacharias.'

'Search the man and the boy,' snapped the centurion as he passed on to the next group.

The soldier ran his hands over Joseph and felt his sash lest he had a knife hidden there; then he did the same to Jesus, saying, 'What about you, are you going to start a revolution?'

Jesus and his mother

On the journey to Jerusalem

The meeting at Jerusalem

John and Jesus in the Temple

'No,' laughed Jesus.

'Sure you're not one of these knife-men we hear about?'

'I'm going to have a carpenter's knife when I get back from the Passover.'

'Well, you be careful what you do with it,' said the soldier and after bidding them good night he went off.

Joseph, Mary and Jesus gathered round the fire. Joseph took the bread and before he broke it he blessed it.

'Blessed art Thou, O Lord our God, King of the world, who bringeth forth bread from the earth.'

The streets of Jerusalem were thronged with people who had come for the Passover. Up and down the temple steps they passed: priests, merchants, money changers, scribes, foreign pilgrims and sightseers, and among them stood old Zacharias with his wife Elizabeth and his son John, searching the faces of all newcomers, hoping soon to see their cousins from Nazareth.

Zacharias recalled how on these very steps thirteen years before the people had waited for him to bless them and he could not speak. He had been struck dumb because he had doubted the word of an angel who had appeared to him at the temple altar. The angel had told him that, old though he and his wife were, they would have a son called John.

'But God forgave you, father; He gave you back your voice when I was born,' broke in John to whom the story was very familiar.

'Yes,' said Elizabeth, 'when you were eight days old your father took you in his arms and suddenly he spoke. Oh, the blessing it was to hear his voice after those long, silent months—loud and strong and praising God.'

Zacharias put his hand on his son's head. 'And blessing you, my son,' he said, 'who will be a prophet of the Most High and go before the face of the Lord to prepare His ways.'

At that moment Elizabeth suddenly saw her cousin Mary, with Joseph and Jesus, coming towards them through the thronging people. Jesus broke away and wandered off to sit by a scribe, fascinated by his writing.

Mary and Elizabeth embraced, and the two men greeted each other. While they talked John slipped through the crowds to where his cousin sat by the scribe.

'I'm John,' he said. 'Peace unto you.'

Jesus jumped to his feet, delighted to meet his cousin at last. 'Unto you also peace.'

The two boys had much to say to each other, and Jesus explained that he hoped to be a carpenter, while John said he thought he would not become a priest like his father. He would rather be in the country than in the temple. Then they heard their mothers calling them, and Jesus went forward to greet Elizabeth rather shyly, before the men and boys went up the steps to the temple.

'Mother, I'll go in with John,' said Jesus.

'Yes, John will go ahead of you,' said Mary, and she and Elizabeth watched as Jesus followed John into the temple, where Joseph and Zacharias awaited them.

'John will go ahead of you,' echoed Elizabeth softly. 'Oh, Mary.' Her cousin put her arm round her understandingly. 'God is very good. I was afraid I might not live to see the day when our boys would meet.'

They sat together on the steps, and Elizabeth, who was an old woman now, told Mary how John liked to go off by himself. 'Sometimes he'll go off into the hills for days at a time, no food, no coat. It's not that he's unhappy, but he likes to be by himself. Is Jesus like that?'

'No,' said Mary, smiling at the thought of her son. 'He's not like that. He's thoughtful and quiet enough sometimes, but for the most part he loves to be among people. In Nazareth he talks to everyone: soldiers, rabbis, beggars. He even makes friends with tax collectors.'

The two women laughed. 'You should have seen his face,' went on Mary, 'when he saw Jerusalem for the first time—so full of wonder and joy. He stood quite still gazing at it. Then he stretched out his arms as though to gather the whole city to him.'

'As he will, Mary, as he will,' said Elizabeth.

'Then he was off, of course,' went on Mary, 'running here, there and everywhere, looking, asking, exploring.' She paused, then turned to Elizabeth. 'We both have good sons.'

'The hope of Israel rests on them,' said Elizabeth softly.

They sat on together in the sunshine, while from inside the temple they could hear the choir singing a psalm and the words, 'Redeemer of Israel.'

When the Passover festival was over the two families left the city together. Elizabeth was tired and Mary had insisted that she should ride part of the way on their ass. But all too soon came the time when they must part, Elizabeth with her husband and son to their home in the nearby Judean hills, and the others to make the long journey back to Nazareth.

'Will you manage to walk the rest of the way?' Mary asked Elizabeth.

'Oh, yes,' said her cousin. 'I shall manage with John's shoulder to lean on. John! Oh, I hope he hasn't wandered off.'

They had thought the two boys were with the men, but Joseph and Zacharias came up without them. However, they were closely followed by some boys who sang and shouted, while one of them played a reed-pipe. John broke away from them, and ran up to his parents, but Jesus was not with him.

'I was looking for him,' he said, 'but when I couldn't find him I made sure he'd be with you.'

'Where did you last see him?' asked Joseph, anxiously.

'I haven't seen him since we left the temple.'

Mary recognized the boy with the pipe as a friend of Jesus' from Nazareth. 'Tell me,' she asked, 'was Jesus with you along the road?'

'Jesus?' replied the boy. 'No, I haven't seen him,' and then seeing Mary's anxious face, 'is he lost?'

John offered to go back to the city to look for Jesus, but Mary said he must help his mother home for there might be robbers on the road after dark. She covered her face with her hands as she said it, overcome at the thought of night coming, and Jesus still missing.

'We must go back,' she said to Joseph. 'It may be only a little way. You know how he stops to talk to people. We may find him with those shepherds we passed, or the vine dressers.'

So together, they set off again towards Jerusalem, while Zacharias, Elizabeth and John went slowly on their way.

In Jerusalem Jesus had forgotten the passing hours. There was so much to see, so much to learn. It was as though he could not tear himself away from the temple. As he stood again in the 'Court of the Gentiles' he saw a blind man tapping his way across the crowded court with his stick. Jesus took his hand and led him to a bench, then stared with compassion at the sightless face.

'Thank you,' said the man. 'You're a good lad. I thought I knew my way about this court well enough—been coming here since I was your size—but there's such a crowd at Passover time, I lose my direction.'

'Were you blind when you were a boy?' asked Jesus.

'Born blind,' said the man with a shrug. 'It's the will of God.'

'It *could* not be the will of God,' said Jesus. Suddenly, from the temple steps came angry shouts. Jesus jumped to his feet. A man, a foreigner by his dress, was being hustled down the steps by two of the temple guards. Across the inner court they dragged him and threw him down close to where Jesus stood.

'Gentile dog, you deserve to die for this,' shouted a guard angrily; and one of the learned elders wailed, 'He has profaned our holy temple—he should die.'

A crowd had gathered and there were cries of 'Stone him—stone the godless heathen.'

Jesus pushed his way to the front of the mob and looked with horror at the cruel faces and then at the stranger who had been forced to his knees.

'Have mercy,' he was crying. 'Have mercy. I did not know. I cannot read your language.'

The temple guard pulled him roughly to his feet. 'Get out then, you Gentile dog, and don't dare to enter God's holy place again.' The terrified man ran off and the crowd dispersed slowly.

Jesus went up to the guard.

'What had that man done?' he asked.

'What had he done? He had dared to enter the House of God.'

'And for that he must be punished?'

The guard glared at him. 'Don't say *you* can't read either.' And he pointed to a great notice on the wall:

NO NON-JEW IS PERMITTED TO PASS
THIS BOUNDARY POINT. ANYONE WHO DOES,
DOES AT HIS OWN RISK, AND WILL BE
LIABLE TO THE DEATH PENALTY

'Blessed be the Lord God of Israel . . .' Jesus turned, the voice
came across the now quiet courtyard and he saw a group of elders
sitting with a scribe who was reading from the scriptures. Slowly,
Jesus walked over to the group and stood by a pillar, listening.

'Blessed be the Lord God of Israel,' read the scribe, 'who only
doeth wondrous things. And blessed be His glorious name for ever,
and let the whole earth be filled with His glory—' he broke off
aware of the boy standing listening. An elder spoke.

'You may come and listen, my son,' he said.

Jesus stepped firmly into the centre of the group.

'Master,' he said, 'I should like to ask you a question.'

'Ask, my son,' replied the elder.

'Why do we speak always of the "Lord God of Israel"? Is not
God the Father of all men?'

'The Father of all? He is the one God, Creator of all and Lord
of Israel,' said the elder.

'Then since he made all,' went on Jesus, 'He is the Lord of all
and Father of all men. Are not all men made of His image?'

The elder agreed.

'Then,' said Jesus, 'men of all nations are our brothers, for the
scriptures say, "All nations whom Thou hast made shall come and
worship before Thee."'

'My son,' said the elder gravely, 'the Gentiles have turned their
backs upon the Lord God and have not listened to His Holy
Commandments. They set up graven images and seek to destroy
God's chosen people. You cannot call the ungodly your brothers.'

'But, master,' insisted Jesus, 'we ask our Father in Heaven to
forgive us our sins. Should we not therefore love those that sin
against us and forgive them? How can we say we have God for our
Father if we do not show to others the mercy He has shown to us?'

The elder was silent. But the scribe spoke rather sternly.

'My son, the Most High God created some to be Jews and some to be Gentiles. Do not, in your zeal, question the wisdom of His ways.'

'I know my Father's wisdom,' said Jesus simply, 'and I know His love.'

Joseph and Mary had wearily retraced their steps to Jerusalem, and now, having searched the city, they entered the temple.

'Back where we started,' said Joseph. 'We've searched every inch of the way. What can have become of him?'

Even while he spoke Mary's quick eyes had seen the group of elders and the boy sitting in the midst of them.

'Joseph—look!' she said, and they both stood silent, watching.

Jesus had taken a scroll from the scribe. Across the court they heard his young voice:

'Here is the verse, master. "When the stranger who is not of thy people Israel shall come and pray in this house, then hear thou from the Heavens that all the people of the earth may know that this house which I have built is called by thy name."' The boy looked up at the learned men. 'That is what the wise Solomon said about the temple of God—that it should be a house of prayer for all people. Why, masters, no earthly father shuts the door against his child whatever bad thing he may have done. Is it likely that our Heavenly Father would show less mercy?'

There was silence. Shyly, Joseph approached and called, 'Jesus! Your mother and I were looking for you.'

Jesus turned with a smile and, after bowing to the elders, ran to his mother.

'Jesus,' said Mary as she embraced him. 'Oh, my son, your father and I have been so anxious. Why did you do this? We have been searching everywhere for you.'

'But, mother,' said Jesus, 'why did you need to search? Didn't you know that I must be in my Father's House?'

And he went back with them to Nazareth and was obedient to his parents, while his mother kept all these sayings in her heart. And as he grew Jesus increased in wisdom and in favour with God and man.

PART 2

The Beloved Son

WHEN JOHN, the son of Zacharias and Elizabeth, grew up he did not become a priest like his father. Instead he went into the wilderness, and into the country round about Jordan, preaching of the Kingdom of God, and urging the people to repent, to ask for forgiveness of their sins, and to be baptized in the river Jordan.

He was a fine, vigorous-looking man, though gaunt and ragged in his rough tunic and leather girdle. He lived a solitary life, save when the people flocked out from Judea and from Jerusalem, some anxious to hear him and to be baptized, and some curious to know what he looked like and what he would say. There were a few who had come from even farther afield. Two young fishermen, John bar Zebedee and Andrew bar Jonah, had come all the way from Galilee to hear him and to be baptized.

One day, when John was preaching on the banks of the river Jordan, he noticed that there were Sadducees and Pharisees among the crowd. These powerful men were the religious leaders of the country and they had been sent from Jerusalem to hear this new 'prophet' and report on him.

'Repent,' cried John, in a voice which made all listen. 'Repent, for the Kingdom of Heaven is at hand. I urge you, people of Judea, do not delay. Do not continue in your wickedness but repent and be cleansed. For the judgment of the Lord is near, and He will destroy the wicked but gather to Him those that do truly turn from their sins.'

The Pharisees and Sadducees moved nearer to hear him.

'Children of Israel,' went on John, 'you pride yourselves on being God's chosen people. But do not be deceived. God is not mocked. I tell you He can see into your very hearts. He will judge you by your thoughts and words and deeds. Every one of you, be you rich or poor, Pharisee or tax collector, learned or ignorant, every one of you must meet His wrath or His mercy, for He will come to the world He has made like a farmer to his harvest, who gathers the wheat into his barns but casts the chaff into the fire to be burned. Repent, therefore, repent now—to-day—before it is too late, for the Kingdom of Heaven is already very near.'

As he finished speaking the crowd surged forward, and a great cry went up, begging for baptism, begging for forgiveness from sins, hailing him as a second prophet Elijah. Cry after cry went up, as, with arms uplifted, they begged for baptism. And standing quietly in the crowd was Jesus, now a young man.

John's voice rang out above the cries: 'Listen, good people. I come to tell you God's will and to prepare the way for His Kingdom. I only baptize you with water, but one will come after me, whose sandals I am not worthy to unloose. He shall baptize you with the Holy Spirit.'

Close beside Jesus stood a Pharisee and a Sadducee, cut off from John by the crowd. 'What does he say?' asked the Pharisee, and the Sadducee, a worldly and cynical man, answered: 'That one greater than he will come. I suppose he means the Messiah.'

The Pharisee gave a sigh of relief. 'Ah, that is important, I have been here every day and I have never heard him say that before. I was beginning to fear he claimed to be the Messiah himself.'

'You Pharisees,' exclaimed the Sadducee scornfully. 'Always on the look-out for blasphemy, yet still expecting an earthly Messiah. How you expect the one to come without the other I really can't imagine.'

'What do you mean?' said the indignant Pharisee.

'Why, it is your party that encourages these "prophets." Every ignorant fanatic in the country is free to preach and rant in the open

Mary and Joseph returning to Jerusalem to search for Jesus

Jesus with the elders

John preaching by the river Jordan

'This is my beloved son in whom I am well pleased'

air, promising Heaven, threatening with Hell. Already people are saying that this one may be the Messiah. Soon he'll be saying it himself. It's a short step from baptist to prophet and from prophet to Messiah by your way of teaching. Yet you are the first to complain of blasphemy.'

'It's plain you know nothing of our teaching,' said the Pharisee, struggling to control his anger.

'Do you not teach,' retorted the Sadducee, 'that the Messiah will come as an ordinary man?'

'Not as *ordinary* man—royal—' said the Pharisee, nearly bursting with rage. The Sadducee gave a mocking smile as he interrupted.

'I know: "of the Royal line of David." But a *man* all the same. It's not safe, you know. The Romans don't like it. The priests don't like it. You'd do better to follow our example.'

To the Pharisee this was the final insult, for the Sadducees grew rich at the expense of their fellow countrymen.

'*Me*,' he shouted, 'follow the example of the Sadducees? Traitors to Israel, friends of Rome!'

But it was the Sadducee who coolly had the last word.

'At least we take the world as it comes,' he said, 'and do not seek a Messiah in the wilderness.' And as he moved away from the angry Pharisee John's voice was heard again.

'I am but a messenger sent to prepare the way. The voice of one crying in the wilderness, make ready the way of the Lord.'

Two soldiers of Herod's army had pushed forward in the crowd and now stood beside Jesus. One of them, a young lad, was much moved by John's words, but his companion was older and tougher.

'Don't be a fool, man,' he said. 'What do you want to get mixed up with this fellow for? He's a madman, dangerous too.'

'But supposing he's right?' asked the other. 'Suppose he's a prophet sent by God? I've no wish to be caught with my sins on my head.'

'And do you think getting yourself wet in the river Jordan is going to save you? Don't you know that this man has been talking against King Herod? If *he* were to hear that you'd been baptized by this John, you'd lose your job, and your head too, I shouldn't wonder.'

But the young soldier was unconvinced, still not knowing what to do, and the two moved nearer John to see if they could speak to him. Jesus followed.

Many in the crowd were begging to be baptized, and calling out that they repented.

'It is not enough to *say* repent,' cried John. 'You must show by your deeds that you intend to lead a new life.'

A Pharisee interrupted. 'My son,' he said, 'do you not exaggerate when you speak of a *new* life? There are many whose lives are already righteous. Do not forget we are the chosen people; we keep the law of Moses and we have Abraham for our forefather.'

'That will not save you from the judgment that is to come,' said John, 'for I tell you, God could raise up children to Abraham from these very stones.'

There was a gasp of astonishment and some laughter from the crowd and a woodcutter declared that John was mad. John turned to the woodcutter.

'I tell you, the time is short,' he said. 'The axe lies already at the foot of the tree, and as you know well enough, every tree that does not bear fruit is cut down and thrown into the fire.'

There were more cries for baptism, and one man threw himself down on the ground at John's feet.

'I am a sinner,' he cried. 'Lord have mercy on me. I am a sinner and the Lord will cast me away.'

'What is your name, friend?' asked John quietly.

'Levi of Capernaum.'

'It's Levi,' said John bar Zebedee turning to his friend Andrew. 'Levi, the tax gatherer from home.'

'A tax gatherer,' cried the woodcutter maliciously. 'Oho, you're for the fire all right.' And he turned and shouted to the crowd. 'See here, a publican on his knees to John the Baptist.'

Ready for any change of mood, the excited crowd responded with angry cries, for the 'publicans' who collected heavy taxes for the Romans were a hated class. 'Thief!' they shouted. 'Traitor!—tool of Rome!'

John put a hand on Levi's shoulder and bent to hear his words.

'I am a sinner,' said the little man humbly. 'A tax gatherer as they say. I suppose, like all holy men, you despise me.'

John replied that he was not a holy man, only a messenger, and that nobody would be despised in God's Kingdom and nobody who truly repented would be shut out.

'What must I do? Change my job?'

'No, but do it honestly. Take no more tax than is due, and don't fill your own purse. This way you will show by your deeds that you truly repent.'

'And will I be forgiven?' asked Levi. John paused before he answered. The Pharisee and the Sadducee exchanged glances. If John claimed to forgive sins he would be guilty of blasphemy.

Then John answered in a strong voice, 'God alone can forgive. But it is His will that you turn from your sins and be baptized by water.'

The young soldier pushed his way forward.

'Sir, I'm a poor man, but I try to do my duty. What more should I do?'

John smiled as he answered, 'Bully no one, blackmail no one and be content with your pay.' This answer delighted the rich Sadducee, who said that the Governor himself could not have given better.

'Let each man be content with what he has,' he said, smoothing his elegant robes.

John turned and looked directly at him. 'Let each man *share* what he has.' The smile left the Sadducee's face.

'Let rich men like you share with men who are poor. If you have two coats give one to a man who has none. If you have food, share it with a man who is hungry. It is deeds like these that will show that you repent.' The crowd surged forward with cries of 'Baptize me, John. Master, baptize me.'

Angrily the Sadducee demanded, 'What right have you to baptize these people? Who do you think you are? The Messiah?'

'I am not the Messiah.'

'Well, then, are you Elijah?'

'I am not.'

'But you are that mysterious prophet of the scriptures?'

'No.'

'Then who are you?'

There was an expectant hush. John did not see Jesus standing there listening as he made his reply.

'I am a voice crying in the wilderness, "Make straight in the desert a highway for our God." For after me comes one who shall baptize with the Holy Spirit and with fire.'

Another great cry went up from the crowd and John walked down to the river followed by Levi and many other penitents.

'Look at them,' said the Sadducee, 'up to their waists in dirty water at the command of a religious maniac.'

The young soldier hesitated. He did not want to make a fool of himself. It was John bar Zebedee, the young fisherman who spoke to him. He told him that he and Andrew had left their nets and come all the way from Galilee to be baptized by John. Three weeks they'd been away from their work and they meant to stay. The young soldier was much impressed. Turning to Jesus he asked:

'Have you been baptized, sir?'

'Not yet,' said Jesus, smiling at him; and he took off his robe and went towards the water. The lad, convinced at last, followed him.

John had just baptized Levi. When he looked up and saw Jesus coming towards him he smiled in astonished recognition. Jesus entered the water and clasped John's hand.

'Jesus,' said the Baptist. 'Do you come to me? It is I who need to be baptized of you.'

'Let it be so now, John,' Jesus replied. 'It is right that you and I should do the will of God.'

So John baptized Jesus and as he did so there was a rumble of thunder, and the sky grew dark.

Some of the crowd on the banks cried out in fear.

'What does it mean, John?' asked Andrew.

'I think it's a sign from Heaven,' said the young fisherman. Only Jesus and John the Baptist heard another sound, a noise like the rushing of birds' wings.

'God has spoken,' said John in a whisper, and he seemed to be listening as he looked up at the wild sky.

'This is my beloved Son in whom I am well pleased!'

Jesus, too, heard the voice and he prayed: 'Father in Heaven, may Thy Kingdom come and Thy will be done on earth as it is in Heaven.'

Led by the Holy Spirit Jesus left the Jordan and went into the wilderness and he was there for forty days without food.

Jesus went into the wilderness

. . . and he was there for forty days without food

The temptation in the wilderness

'The wilderness' was the name given to the country round about the Dead Sea—it might have been called the 'Dead Land.' A few hungry jackals prowled among the sun-baked rocks, and sometimes a snake slithered over the stony ground, but apart from these there was no life—no vegetation, no shelter, only stark white rock as far as the eye could see. Sometimes a bird of prey hovered beneath the burning blue sky, its keen eye scanning the glaring rocks for any sign of life, but more often the vulture would come seeking the dead.

To this place came Jesus after his baptism, the words he had heard still ringing in his ears: 'This is my beloved son in whom I am well pleased.' As he prayed he was conscious of another voice. 'You are the Son of God, Jesus, the Messiah. What are you going to do? How are you going to begin?'

'Father,' prayed Jesus, 'show me the way. Let me not fall into temptation. Not my will but Thine be done.'

He was faint with hunger. As he tried to rise he stumbled and his hand clutched some loose stones. The words beat in his brain: 'You are starving—you need bread.' He looked at the stone in his hand which seemed to mock him by having the appearance of a small loaf. Very persuasively came the voice again. 'If you are the Son of God, command these stones that they become bread.' He was tempted. Should he? Should he so use the power God had given him? Is this what God would wish him to do?

'Why not? If you are the Son of God you have the power to turn stones to bread, to make the barren lands fertile, to make your country a land of plenty. It is written in the scriptures: "The glowing sand shall become a pool, and the thirsty ground springs of water: in the habitation of jackals shall be grass with reeds and rushes."'

In the fierce sun Jesus looked round at the parched rocks. He was tempted.

'Father, Thy will be done,' he cried out in the silence.

'Turn the stone to bread.' Was it God? Was it the Father who spoke? Or was it the devil tempting him?

'Feed yourself, then feed your people. Feed the hungry. You are hungry now. Think of the others who are hungry. How they would flock to you if you could give them bread.'

Suddenly to Jesus came the answer he sought. He threw down the stone and stood erect.

'It is written: "Man shall not live by bread alone; but by every word of God."'

Stronger for his resistance Jesus climbed higher into the barren hills, the hot wind blowing his hair and robe. Standing on a rocky ledge he looked westward towards Jerusalem. In the distance he could see a shimmering green patch—the olive trees surrounding the Holy City. In his mind's eye he saw the pinnacles of the temple dominating the green hills.

'Jerusalem.'

The inner voice was only a whisper now: 'Oh, Jerusalem, Jerusalem, you that stone the prophets and kill the messengers of God.'

'Father,' prayed Jesus, 'is that the way I must go? A man of sorrows?'

The whisper became more insistent. 'If you are the Son of God, the people will want a sign. How will they know that you are the son of God? You heard—or thought you heard the voice of God—'

Yes, he'd heard it. He would not doubt. 'This is my beloved Son.'

'Yes, but only you and John heard that voice. To the rest you are Jesus of Nazareth, the carpenter's son. You must *prove* that you are the Son of God.'

His prayer was almost a cry: 'Father, forsake me not utterly!' Relentlessly the voice continued, 'Look down there at Jerusalem.'

Jesus looked again towards the beloved city.

'The people believe that the Messiah will appear on the pinnacle of the temple. Go now into Jerusalem, climb to the highest pinnacle and throw yourself down. For the scriptures say: "He shall give his angels charge over thee and they shall hold thee up lest thou dash thy foot against a stone."'

The scriptures did say that. Was this the proof God promised His Messiah? He was tempted. But suddenly another verse from the scriptures leapt into his mind and in his relief he called aloud: 'The scriptures also say, "Thou shalt not put the Lord Thy God to the proof."'

After this Jesus climbed to the top of a very high mountain, so high that it seemed as though he was above the whole world. He felt very close to his Father as he prayed: 'Father, I know that of myself I can do nothing, that Thine is the power as Thine the glory. I know that Thou wilt guide me so that I may guide Thy people to a knowledge of Thy Kingdom. Help me to feed them, not with the bread that perishes, but with the bread of life that they may live abundantly in Thy love. Help me to show that the Son of Man came not to be served but to serve and to give his life as a ransom for many. For Thine is the Kingdom and the power and the glory.'

Very softly came the whisper, '*Thine* is the kingdom, the power and the glory. *Thine.* God has given the power to *you*. Remember what the scriptures say—"Thou art my Son. This day have I begotten thee. Ask of me and I will give thee the nations for thine inheritance and the uttermost parts of the earth for thy possession."'

From the high mountain Jesus looked down over his country. The voice persisted, 'Think of your suffering people ruled by a heathen power—they look for a king to save them. King of Israel. That is the Messiah they look for.'

Jesus drew himself up and his lips formed the words, 'King of Israel!'

'And not only of Israel, of other nations too. All the nations of the world God has given to you.'

Wonderingly Jesus turned towards the east.

'Think of those other kingdoms who do not know the true God. Rich and powerful kingdoms, paying homage to *you*. All this power, and the glory of these kingdoms could be *yours* if you will serve them as a *King*.'

King of Israel? Ruler of all the nations of the world? Would he not then indeed establish God's Kingdom on earth? This was the greatest temptation. And then suddenly it was as though Satan himself was speaking: 'Take my way. Fall down and pay homage to me.'

Strength seemed to flow back into his weary body, and in a flash he knew the power that had tempted him and raised these pictures before his eyes.

'Get thee behind me, Satan,' he commanded. 'For it is written, "Thou shalt pay homage to the Lord thy God and Him only shalt thou serve."'

There was dead silence over the mountain and a great peace

descended on Jesus. Temptation had left him for the time being and it was with joy he spoke the now familiar words,

'For Thine is the Kingdom and the power and the glory.'

After this Jesus returned to Galilee with the power of the spirit upon him.

On the shores of Lake Galilee, sometimes called the Sea of Tiberias, a group of fishermen were talking as they hauled in their boat. Zebedee, the owner of the boat, with his two sons James and John and his hired men, had been out for a night's fishing. Their friends Simon and Andrew bar Jonah sometimes fished with them, but to-day they had been casting their nets nearer the shore. Simon grumbled at the poor catch, saying that when fish had been plentiful he'd been a whole month on his own, while Andrew had been in Judea following John the Baptist.

'And what good's it done?' grumbled Simon. 'The man's been put in prison for all his fine words, and who's the better off?'

'We'll all be better off when the Kingdom comes,' said his brother.

'Listen, Andrew,' said Simon. 'I've heard that talk of kingdoms before and it's dangerous talk.' He told them of another preacher, a countryman of theirs, who some years before had been put to death for preaching of the Kingdom of God, and hundreds of men of Galilee had been crucified with him.

'These very roads were lined with their crosses,' he said. 'As an example it was, as a warning to the people. I'll not forget those crosses as long as I live.'

John and Andrew assured him that although John was in prison there was another greater than he, who would baptize with the Holy Spirit. Simon was shocked at this and said that this too was dangerous talk, but they went on eagerly to explain that they hoped to find a man called Jesus of Nazareth, since they believed him to be the one John heralded.

'That's why we came back,' said Andrew. 'It's not far from here to Nazareth.'

'Oh,' said Simon, with a laugh, 'so that's why you came home— not to give your poor brother a hand with the fishing, but to wait for this Jesus of Nazareth.'

At that moment Zebedee called to his sons from the boat and they hurried to help him, while Simon and Andrew cast their nets once more into the water.

Simon was the first to notice a tall man standing by the water's edge looking at them, and when Andrew turned to look, he gripped Simon's arm excitedly.

'It's the one I told you of,' he shouted. 'It's Jesus.'

He waded to the shore as Jesus beckoned to him. Simon followed more slowly.

Andrew was so excited he could hardly speak at first.

'Oh, master,' he said at last, 'you have come to us. You won't know me—I'm Andrew bar Jonah—but I was at the river Jordan the day you came to be baptized.'

Jesus said that he remembered him. 'The time that John told you of has come,' he said. 'Will you put your trust in the good news, and follow me?'

'Master, I will,' said Andrew; then he turned to present his brother to him.

'Simon,' said Jesus, 'how has the catch been?'

Simon was rather taken aback by this homely question, but it put him at his ease.

'Sir,' he said, 'we have toiled all night and have caught nothing.'

'Simon,' said Jesus again, 'will you leave your nets and follow me? I will make you a fisher of men.'

But Simon was suddenly overawed by the presence of Jesus. 'Leave me,' he said, 'for I am a sinful man.'

Jesus reassured him with a hand on his broad shoulder. From now on, he said, Simon would be working for the Kingdom of God, and though he might toil for many days and catch nothing, he would never despair, for his faith was as firm as a rock. He would be a faithful fisher of men, casting his net not for fish which would perish, but for the hearts of men. And Simon, not quite understanding, none the less resolved to follow Jesus wherever he went.

Jesus smiled at him, and turned to look at the other fishermen who were mending their nets by their father's boat. Andrew called them, and they looked up. Then Jesus too called them by name and they came running.

John had recognized Jesus, and he called out excitedly as he ran up: 'Master, master, oh master, you have come.' He grasped the hand Jesus offered him, and went on quickly, 'We looked for you and could not find you, and now you have found us.' He turned to James. 'It is Jesus, James. This is Jesus.'

Jesus asked if the boat was theirs, and James replied that it belonged to their father, Zebedee, for whom they worked.

'Will you come,' asked Jesus, 'and work for your Father in Heaven, and like Andrew and Simon become fishers of men?'

'We will, master,' they said together without hesitation.

Jesus smiled at them. 'Your voices are strong and you are quick to follow,' he said. 'You shall be known as Sons of Thunder.'

Then Simon asked if Jesus would come to their house and eat—his wife would prepare a meal.

So Jesus set off along the beach with his four new disciples. They came to a village street, and presently reached Simon's house and all went in together. From the door Simon called for his wife, but a weak voice spoke and he crossed the room to where his mother-in-law lay on a raised shelf, too ill to rise. It was the fever again, she said, and Simon's wife had gone for a doctor. Simon turned to Jesus in apology: after all there was no one to wait on him.

Jesus crossed the room to the bed. He sat by the old woman, and took her hand as she tossed and murmured. In a moment she became calm. She opened her eyes and looked at Jesus. He smiled at her.

'Will you rise and wait on us, mother?' he asked gently.

She felt her forehead with one hand while the other remained in his. 'It has gone—the fever has left me,' she said incredulously. 'Who are you, sir?'

'I'm a friend of Simon and Andrew,' Jesus said. He helped her to her feet, and she kissed his hand in gratitude before she hurried off to prepare the meal. Jesus and three of the disciples sat on the ground, while Simon brought a bowl of water for Jesus to wash his hands. Then the others did the same, while the old woman served them with bread, figs, wine and the best that the house could offer.

While they ate, John asked how they would know when the Kingdom of God had come.

'It has come already, John,' said Jesus. 'It has come among you. And through you it will be made known to the world.'

The Sea of Galilee

'Leave your nets and follow me'

'I will make you fishers of men'

Simon was amazed at this, saying they were only poor fishermen, with no power, no learning even; to which Jesus replied that all the power came from God, and His Kingdom did not depend upon learned men. Nor did He need riches and glory as did earthly kings.

'But, master,' John argued, 'John preached that the Kingdom would come suddenly upon us with judgment and glory and that God would smite the wicked and raise up the repentant. We thought—I thought—that the whole world would change when God set up His Kingdom on earth.'

'It will change, John,' replied Jesus, 'but not suddenly and not in the way you think. A farmer sows seed in the ground, but he does not know how it grows and springs up. For the earth brings forth the harvest of itself: first the blade of corn, then the ear, and after that the full corn in the ear. That is the way the Kingdom will grow. Quietly and in secret.'

Simon still looked puzzled and concerned. 'Lord, I do not understand this,' he said. 'How can we, poor fishermen, bring men to such a Kingdom?'

'By your faith and example,' said Jesus. He looked around at the four faces. 'You still do not understand this? How can I explain it to you.' He picked up a loaf of bread, and asked if they knew how it was prepared.

Simon gave a doubtful look at his mother-in-law before he said yes. It was clear that bread-making was something with which he did not concern himself. So Jesus called on the old lady to explain. At first she was too shy to speak, but she was pleased at being asked.

'Well,' she said slowly, 'first I take flour. . . .'

'How much?' asked Jesus, helping her.

'Three measures—and I mix it with water.'

'And what is it like then?' questioned Jesus.

'It is dough, sir—a small heavy lump of dough.'

'And what makes it light and good to eat?' asked Jesus.

'It's the cooking,' burst in Simon, thinking at last he had the answer. 'It's the baking in the oven.'

Jesus smiled at the old woman. 'Is that all, mother?' he asked.

She gave him a smile in return. 'Oh, no, sir,' she said. 'It's the yeast I put in the dough. I set it aside and the yeast makes the dough rise and become good bread.'

'So you see, Simon,' said Jesus, 'the Kingdom of God is like the yeast that a woman takes and hides in three measures of flour, and the yeast works through the flour until the whole loaf is leavened.'

James was clearly disappointed at this explanation. 'A quiet Kingdom, growing secretly,' he murmured; 'that's not what people expect.'

But John was carried away by the idea. 'I understand,' he said. 'The Kingdom is with us, among us, now. And, as the seed grows in the earth and the yeast works in the bread, so will the Kingdom grow among us until the world is filled with its glory.'

Simon was sober at the thought. 'God's Kingdom in the hands of four fishermen,' he said thoughtfully. 'It doesn't seem right. And yet—' and he looked directly at Jesus as he spoke, 'I believe you, master.'

But Andrew, like James, was a little disappointed. 'Is that all, master?' he asked. 'No judgment, no Heaven? Is the Kingdom just a secret working of good among men?'

The disciples watched Jesus intently as he answered.

'It is among you,' he said, 'and awaiting you. You are fishermen, so understand when I tell you this. The Kingdom of Heaven is also like a net cast into the sea and catching fish of every kind. What do you do when the net is full?'

They dragged it up on the beach, they told him, and then sat down and collected the good fish in the baskets.

'And is it all good fish?' asked Jesus, and they told him no, they threw away the bad.

'It will be the same at the end of the world,' said Jesus. 'There will be good men and wicked men, and the wicked will be picked out from among the good and cast away, but the good will be gathered into the Kingdom. Do you understand?'

He put his hands on the shoulders of Simon and John, who sat on either side of him, and looked affectionately at them all.

'Do not be afraid, little flock,' he said, 'for it is your Father's good pleasure to give you the Kingdom.'

PART 3

Jesus the Healer

Now when Jesus heard that John the Baptist had been thrown into prison by King Herod, he went about Galilee with his four disciples preaching the good news of the Kingdom of Heaven and healing all manner of disease among the people so that his fame spread and he was followed by great crowds.

He stayed near Capernaum, at the house of Simon and Andrew, and when the people learnt that he was there they flocked to the little house.

Jesus sat in the crowded room with his four disciples while those who could not get in pressed against the door. Simon's mother-in-law was worried by so many people, and she tried to drive them away.

'You cannot come in,' she said. 'The house is quite full already, and the rabbi should be resting. I must close the door now. I am sorry, but there is no room.'

'Wait,' called a scribe, pushing his way to the front of the crowd. 'We come from Jerusalem, and wish to speak with this teacher. Is he there?'

Simon's mother-in-law was impressed by this important visitor. 'Yes, sir,' she said doubtfully. 'He is, but I don't think you can see him. There are so many round him.'

But the scribes pushed past her and forced their way towards Jesus.

Meanwhile four more men had joined the crowd outside the door of the house. They were carrying a litter on which lay their friend.

James Alphaeus, one of the men in the crowd, asked what was wrong with the man on the litter.

'Paralysed,' said Philip, one of the bearers. 'Thinks this Jesus can cure him,' and the paralysed man echoed his words.

'He will cure me, sinner though I am,' he cried. 'Take me to Jesus, friends, so that I may be cured.'

The crowd at the door murmured in sympathy, and made way for the litter, while Philip cried to Simon's mother-in-law, 'Don't close the door, mother. There's a man here paralysed. Let us carry him in to Jesus.'

But she refused. Jesus, she said, was talking to the other rabbis, and must be left in peace. She closed the door firmly, leaving them outside. As she turned back into the room a man who stood nearby asked her if it were true that this new teacher could cure all kinds of diseases.

'It is true,' she said. 'I can testify to that. The day my son-in-law brought him home I had the fever on me and he took my hand in his. I'll never forget the feel of it, so gentle and so firm.'

'And the fever left you?'

'It was drawn right out of me,' she answered, and told him of others he had cured. 'Why, the whole of Galilee is talking about him—not only because of the healing, but of the way he teaches. Are you a stranger here, sir, that you haven't heard?'

'Yes,' said the man. 'I come from Kerioth in the south.'

As they spoke he had been trying to catch a glimpse of Jesus through the crowd, and now he worked his way nearer to where Jesus sat and heard him saying, 'Understand, dear children, that God is your Father, and it is His will that you should live in the abundance of His love. Ask and you shall receive. Seek and you shall find. Knock and the door shall be opened to you.'

Among the listeners was a man sitting with his arm round his little boy, both listening attentively.

'Master,' asked the man, 'what is this door you speak of, and how may we find it?'

'It is the door to life,' replied Jesus, 'but it stands in a narrow and difficult road and few men find it. For there is another road, the way of the world, and many tread that way. Thinking their broad highway is the way of life, they pass by the narrow path that leads to God.'

'How may we find it then, master?' asked the man.

'He that seeks shall find,' said Jesus, 'and to everyone that knocks the door is opened, because God is your Father. Would you, if your son were to ask for bread, hand him a stone?'

His listeners murmured and laughed at the idea.

'Or if he asked for a fish,' went on Jesus, 'give him a snake?' The little boy burst out laughing at this suggestion, while Jesus continued, 'No, of course not. Well then, if you, being sinful men, know what is good for your children and give it to them, how much more will your Father in Heaven give good things to those that ask him.'

Meanwhile the crowd still pressed round the door of the house. Some of them had managed to open it a crack, and they could hear the murmured talk within.

'What's he saying, Thaddeus?' called Philip.

'They are all talking and asking questions,' said Thaddeus. 'I can't hear Jesus. Last thing I heard was "To everyone that knocks the door shall be opened."'

There were protests from the crowd at being shut out, and Philip said with a grin, 'It's no good knocking on *this* door. They couldn't get it opened if they tried—there are too many people.'

James Alphaeus asked what else Thaddeus had heard and he told them, '"Ask and you shall receive, seek and you shall find."'

'That's it,' said the paralysed man, 'to seek and to ask.' And while Philip knelt down beside him, he closed his eyes and muttered a prayer, 'Hear my prayer, O Lord, and let my cry come unto thee. Have mercy on me, O God, in thy loving kindness, and in thy tender mercy cleanse me from my sins. Have mercy on me, O Lord, for I am withered away. O Lord heal me, for my bones are weak.'

While he prayed James Alphaeus had climbed up beside the doorway, and he called down to Philip that there was a hole in the roof through which they could both see and hear what was going on inside the house. Philip went over to him. A sudden idea had occurred to him, and he asked if they could make the hole bigger. On being assured that they could, he said he thought they could do more than see and hear.

Inside the house the little boy was now standing by Jesus, who had his arm around him, while he answered one of the scribes, who had leaned forward to ask him: 'What should a man do to inherit eternal life?'

'What is written in the law?' asked Jesus.

' "Thou shalt love the Lord thy God," ' quoted the scribe, ' "with all thy heart and with all thy soul and with all thy mind." And "Thou shalt love thy neighbour as thyself." '

'You have answered rightly,' replied Jesus. 'Do this and you will live.'

'Master,' said the little boy, forgetting his shyness, 'does the law mean that I must love all my neighbours, all the people in the village? Or only my friends?'

'It means much more than that, son,' Jesus told him. 'Since God is the Father of all, all men are your brothers, and as God loves all His children, so must you love them too.'

'Everybody?' asked the boy, trying to take it in.

'The rabbi means all the children of Israel, son.'

Jesus said, 'I mean all the children of God.'

'Oh, come, rabbi,' protested a Pharisee, 'you would not include Samaritans and Gentiles?'

When Jesus did not reply, one of the scribes took up the questioning. 'Who,' he asked, 'is my neighbour?'

'Listen,' said Jesus, 'and I will tell you a story. A certain man was travelling from Jerusalem to Jericho when he was set upon by robbers who stripped him, beat him, and, taking all he had, left him there by the roadside, half dead. And after a while a certain priest came down that same road, and when he saw the man lying there he crossed to the other side of the road and passed him by. Later a Levite came down the road and he also saw the wounded man, but he too passed by on the other side. But a certain Samaritan happened to be going along that road, and when he saw the man he was filled with pity, and he bathed his wounds and bound them and lifted him on to his ass, and brought him to an inn and took care of him. And the next day he gave money to the innkeeper and said, "Take care of him, and if you spend more than I have given

Jesus in Capernaum

'Rise, take up your stretcher and walk'

you, I will repay you when I come back again." ' Jesus paused, and looked at their intent faces. 'Now, which of these three do you think was a good neighbour to the man who fell among robbers?'

'Why,' said the scribe without hesitation, 'the man who treated him with kindness.'

'Go,' said Jesus, 'and do as he did.'

The little boy put the thoughts of them all into words.

'Fancy,' he said wonderingly, 'the Samaritan being the one to help him. Samaritans are our enemies.'

'The law,' said the Pharisee severely, 'has been interpreted: thou shalt love thy neighbour and hate thine enemies.'

'That is not God's law,' said Jesus—and the scribes gasped with surprise at this seeming irreverence. 'I say to you, love your enemies and pray for them that persecute you, so that you may become children of your Father in Heaven, who causes His sun to rise and His rain to fall on the just and the unjust alike. For if you love them that love you, what thanks have you deserved? Even sinners love those that love them. And if you do good to them that do good to you, what thanks have you deserved? Even sinners lend in the hope of repayment. No. Love your enemies, despairing of no one, and you will be sons of the Most High. For He Himself is kind to thankless and to evil men. Be therefore merciful as your Heavenly Father is merciful.'

His listeners fell silent, thinking of what he had said. But suddenly Simon realized that something unusual was going on above their heads.

'Andrew,' he cried, 'the roof! There's someone on the roof.'

Andrew got up quickly, and went over to the place where daylight could be seen coming through.

'They've stripped the turf away,' he said. 'There's a gap as big as a window. Who is it? What are you doing up there?'

All heads were turned up now, watching, and as the hole in the roof was made larger, they stared fascinated; and suddenly the little boy cried out in great excitement, 'Look—look, there's a man coming down—a man on a bed.' He took Jesus' hand, anxious that he should share this excitement. 'Master, see—a man coming down through the roof on a bed.'

Jesus rose, and watched silently as the paralysed man was lowered, cautiously and gently. When it was near enough for them to reach it, Simon, Andrew and the other disciples took hold of the stretcher and guided it carefully to the ground, while the crowd talked excitedly, wondering who the man was, and marvelling at this way of getting him in so that he could come to Jesus.

Simon's mother-in-law peered up in consternation. 'Mercy!' she said. 'Whatever next! Just look at our roof!'

Simon reassured her. 'Don't fret, mother, there's no harm done that can't soon be put right. Easy—easy with him—gently now,' he went on, his hand steering the stretcher to its resting place near Jesus. The man on it had his eyes closed, while he murmured a prayer. 'Have mercy on me, O God, in Thy tender mercy, cleanse me from my sins.'

Simon bent over him anxiously. 'How is it with you, friend?' he asked.

'Jesus. Where is Jesus?' asked the man, and Jesus, who was standing on the other side of the stretcher, said gently, 'I am here.'

The man turned his face to him eagerly. 'Master,' he said, 'I am a sinful man, but if you will you can cure me.'

'Be of good cheer, my son,' said Jesus, 'your sins are forgiven you.'

The scribe and the Pharisee put their heads together and talked in shocked whispers.

'This is blasphemy,' said the Pharisee, and the scribe agreed. 'Indeed it is,' he said. 'Who can forgive sins but God alone?'

Jesus looked at them. 'I know what you are thinking,' he said. 'But I will ask you this. Is it easier to say to this poor man, "Your sins are forgiven you" or to say, "Rise, take up your stretcher and walk"? But I will show you that the Son of Man has power on earth to forgive sins.'

While the people watched in breathless silence, Jesus turned to the paralysed man and spoke gently.

'Rise,' he said, and slowly, his eyes fixed upon Jesus, the man sat up.

Jesus held out his hands to the man, who grasped them and got shakily to his feet. Very nervously he tried to walk, afraid to trust his legs, but at last he took a step—then another.

'I can walk,' he said in wonder. 'God be praised. I can *walk*.' And he shouted the good news to his friends on the roof. 'I can walk! I can walk!' They answered with shouts of pleasure and amazement, blessing the name of the Lord, and praising God. The man stooped and kissed Jesus' hand.

'Master,' he said softly, 'I thank you.'

'Pick up your stretcher now,' said Jesus, 'and walk home and give thanks to God.'

The man took up the stretcher with his new-found strength, rolled it up and put it under his arm and as he walked to the door, the people crowded round Jesus and cried out, 'God be praised. He has seen our suffering.'

In a street in Capernaum leading down to the lake, Levi, the tax collector, sat at the 'seat of custom,' with a Roman soldier standing on duty beside him. Levi had a pile of money on the table in front of him and was marking off names on a tablet as the fishermen put money down in payment of taxes.

'Simon and Andrew bar Jonah—five,' said Levi checking the amount. 'Zebedee and sons—twelve. That's all the fishermen,' he said, looking up at the soldier, of whom he was rather afraid. 'It's the farmers next. Philip of Bethsaida—fifteen.'

'Having a good day?' asked the soldier affably.

Levi cringed a little as he answered, not sure how friendly to be to the soldier. 'Good or bad, it's all the same to me,' he said. 'I'm only a tax collector. I only do my job.'

'And what a job,' said Philip scornfully. He was a farmer, come to pay his dues. 'Robbing your own countrymen to pay a foreign power.'

'Careful what you say,' said the soldier, menacingly.

'Oh, it's not your fault, soldier,' said Philip, undaunted. 'You have to obey your Emperor. But this fellow here is a Jew like us. He doesn't have to work for Rome.'

Another farmer joined in with, 'And that's not the worst of it. He makes a profit for himself. Everyone knows how the tax collectors grow rich.'

Philip pointed to the pile of money. 'How much of all that are you keeping for yourself, Levi?'

'None of it,' said Levi indignantly. 'Not a penny.'

There was a burst of unbelieving laughter from those around him, in which the soldier joined, as he said, 'Oh come, you can't get away with that story, you know.'

'It's true,' insisted Levi.

'Didn't I see you at the river Jordan?' asked Andrew.

'That's right,' said Levi eagerly. 'I was baptized.'

'Baptized!' said Philip, scornfully. 'Yet you're still in this job!' He gave a short laugh. 'Here, Levi,' he said, 'Here's your fifteen—five for you and ten for Rome.' And with another laugh he went off.

Levi looked after him, deeply hurt and smouldering with indignation. He looked at the pile of money on the table, and was tempted to take part of it, as he had always done in the old days. As he stretched out his hand to the coins, a shadow fell across the table, and, looking up, Levi saw Jesus standing there. His face lit up in recognition.

'Jesus of Nazareth!' he exclaimed—and instantly ashamed of his desire to take the money, he looked away, unable to meet Jesus' eyes.

Jesus looked at him. 'Follow me,' he said.

Levi could hardly believe his ears. 'Follow you?' he repeated. 'Oh, I will, sir. I'll follow if you'll have me.' He looked down at his table again, then at the soldier. 'Here, soldier,' he said. 'You take over.'

He smiled proudly at the fishermen and farmers standing around, and then he went off with Jesus. The fishermen and farmers looked after them in astonishment and some followed. Others made a dive for the money he had left but the soldier was too quick for them, and stepped in to guard it.

'Stand back, stand back,' he cried pushing them away, and grumbling but good-humoured they went on paying their taxes.

Among those who had watched the conversation between Jesus and Levi were a scribe and a Pharisee.

'You see it is as I said,' said the Pharisee. 'He picks his friends from the riff-raff of the town.'

'Yet he's a man of some learning,' said the scribe.

The Pharisee agreed. 'He's a clever fellow and a dangerous one. Already people are hailing him as a prophet on account of his healing and teaching.'

The scribe was looking towards the town, and now he pointed.

'Look where they are going,' he said, 'into the very lowest quarter of the town.'

'With all the rabble following on his heels,' added the Pharisee scornfully. 'Jesus of Nazareth, the miracle worker! Can you wonder that the town turns out to see him? It's like a pagan circus.'

'Yet all he does,' returned the scribe grudgingly, 'he does in the name of God.'

'Yes,' said the Pharisee. 'That is why he is dangerous. A magician, even a miracle man is soon forgotten. But this man whom they call "Master" not only heals their sick, but makes outcasts his friends, even daring to tell them their sins are forgiven. Why, if he's not stopped he'll strike at the very heart of our law and our religion.'

'He must be stopped.'

'Now?' queried the Pharisee. The other nodded. 'You are willing to follow the rabble?'

'Certainly,' said the scribe. And together they went into the town.

Levi was leading the way through a squalid street. Women stood about gossiping, children sat among the goats and chickens and played games. Jesus and the four disciples followed him, and behind came a crowd of people.

'It's down this street, master,' said Levi. 'First door on the left. I'll go on ahead if you don't mind. There's some rough characters round where I live and I wouldn't want you mixed up with them.' And off he went, pushing his way through the crowd.

Simon turned to Jesus and asked, 'Master, do you know where he's taking you?'

'To his home,' said Jesus.

'But in such a street, master,' protested Simon. 'You don't know this town as I do. Decent people won't be seen around this quarter.'

'I know where I'm going,' said Jesus quietly. Down the narrow arched street he walked and into the doorway of a house.

Inside the house Levi was making frantic efforts to prepare a meal for Jesus. There were jugs of wine ready on the table, where a man sat counting some money. On the floor squatted another man playing a pipe, while a little girl in ear-rings and bracelets danced in the middle of the floor, watched by three more men and two women who clapped their hands in time to her dancing. Two other men were gambling over a game of dice.

Poor Levi was very flustered. As he brought plates of fruit to the table, he turned to the girl and said, 'Stop dancing now and go home, there's a good girl. Here, take this and go.' He gave her some coins from the pile on the table. 'And you too—all of you . . .' he tried to wave the men from his house.

The man with the money protested. 'There now, you've gone and upset the accounts. Giving money away just when I've counted it—what's come over you?'

'Go on—off with you, too,' said Levi in exasperation. 'I've got company coming. Respectable company.'

There was a roar of laughter from the men.

'Respectable? Oho, that's good,' said one of them coming to the table. 'Who've you got coming, Levi, the chief rabbi?' He helped himself to some of the fruit, while they all laughed except Levi, and no one noticed that Jesus had entered the house.

The rest of the men suggested jokingly that perhaps Levi was expecting some of the Pharisees, or even the Roman Governor. The man with the flute beat time and chanted:

> 'Let's all be respectable
> For Levi the Publican.'

'Levi the publican, Levi the publican,' echoed the others, and the man with the flute went on more loudly:

> 'All the best people know
> Levi the Publican
> Levi's GONE RESPECTABLE,'

he bellowed, and they all roared with laughter. The flute player, delighted by his own cleverness and the applause of his friends, began again, picking out the tune. Levi was beside himself, and when he saw Jesus at the door smiling at him he put his head in his hands and cried in his disappointment, 'Oh, master. You oughtn't to have come here. I ought not to have asked you.'

A hush came over his riotous friends. The laughter ceased, the flute player let the tune trail away, and they all looked rather sheepish.

'It's all right, Levi,' said one of them, as they all began to shuffle to the door. 'We're clearing off now.'

But Jesus crossed over to Levi and asked, 'Won't your friends stay, Levi?'

Levi raised his head and looked into Jesus' eyes which were full of laughter. 'You want them to stay?' he asked in amazement.

'Yes,' said Jesus. Levi's spirits rose again and he called to the others to stay for a meal if they wanted to. The men looked at each other with raised eyebrows, then moved back towards the table. The girl got there first, and sidled up to Jesus, speaking to him with a professional whine in her voice.

"I want to,' she said. 'We don't have nothing to eat at our house, sir, and no money to buy bread.' She held out a practised little hand to beg, keeping the other which held the money hidden behind her back.

'Then you must eat now, child,' said Jesus, putting his hand on her head and looking into her eyes. 'See what a feast Levi has prepared for us.'

But one of the men was indignant at her deceit. 'No money to buy bread, eh?' he asked, grabbing her wrist and opening the hand holding the money. 'What about *this*?'

'Give it to me, it's mine,' cried the girl, trying to snatch back the money. 'Levi gave it to me, didn't you, Levi?'

'I gave it to you to go, my girl,' replied Levi, 'but it seems you are going to stay.'

'You said we could stop,' the girl shrilled. '*He* said so too.'

'All right,' said Levi quietening her. 'All right. If you stay mind your manners and don't try your tricks on the master here.' He turned to Jesus. 'Sit down, master, and your friends too.'

Now that they were invited to stay, they all wanted to sit next to Jesus, and the men, all smiles, shook hands with him. The girl squatted at his side. The flute player began to play and the rest began with hearty appetites to eat the food. Levi was beginning to enjoy himself. News of Jesus' presence had spread around the neighbourhood and more and more people pushed into the house, including the scribe and Pharisee.

The girl, warmed by Jesus' kindness, began to talk to him. 'Why do they call you master?' she asked. 'Are you rich?'

'No, not rich,' said Jesus.

'Some of Levi's friends are very rich,' she confided, and added, with a wink, 'tax collectors, you know. I always ask them for money. But I'm sorry I lied to you about it.' Encouraged by his smile she asked if he were a teacher, and when he nodded, she was full of pride.

'Fancy me sitting here talking to a teacher! Down the synagogue they won't have nothing to do with me. They won't let me in because I'm a bad girl. But you seem different somehow, not like them scribes and Pharisees and all that lot.'

'Watch what you're saying, girl,' warned Levi, who had suddenly noticed the scribe and Pharisee standing by the door. He moved over to them. 'I'm very honoured to welcome you, sirs,' said Levi. 'Won't you join us at the table?'

The scribe and the Pharisee did not even look at him, but Levi went on cordially: 'I'm afraid the company's a bit rough—all except him: Jesus of Nazareth, you know, the great prophet.' Levi pointed to where Jesus sat: 'Him in the white.'

'We know Jesus of Nazareth,' they replied frostily.

'You do?' said Levi. 'There now, of course you do. There isn't anybody around Galilee who hasn't heard of him and all the good he's done. Why, he's got more followers than John the Baptist had, and that's saying something. John prophesied that one greater than him would come, you know. Well, it's my belief that it's Jesus he spoke of.'

'You believe that?' broke in the man from Kerioth who had followed the scribe and Pharisee.

'Oh, I do, sir,' replied Levi. 'Why, John as good as said so.'

The man turned to his neighbour. 'You hear that, Thomas?'

'Yes,' Thomas replied. 'But don't get carried away, my friend. Remember what we're come to ask.'

They were interrupted by a burst of laughter from the table, and the voice of Andrew calling out to Levi that he was missing the feast.

'And what a feast,' cried John. 'It's like a marriage party.'

'In a way, John, it *is* a marriage party,' said Jesus.

'Come on, Levi—the master's been asking for you,' said Andrew as he crossed to where Levi stood with the scribe and Pharisee.

Levi was delighted. 'This is Andrew, gentlemen,' he said to the

The feast at Levi's house

The house of Jairus

Jairus' daughter

scribe and Pharisee. 'He was one of the Baptist's men too'—and he hurried to join Jesus at the table.

'I am amazed,' said the Pharisee, 'that men should so quickly turn from one leader to another. The man John, fanatic though he was, at least urged men to think of their sins. To repent—to *fast*.'

'That's true,' said Thomas, interrupting him. 'John made a great point of fasting.'

'But your new master, it seems,' went on the Pharisee scornfully, 'enjoys himself eating and drinking freely with the outcasts of society—tax gatherers, thieves, parasites. . . .'

His voice rose in his contempt, and hearing it the guests fell silent, watching and listening. Levi was not going to have his party spoilt.

'Careful what you're saying,' he protested. 'This is my house. The master is my guest and so are all the others.'

He stopped as he saw Jesus rise to his feet, and at a word from him he and Andrew went slowly to the table and stood beside him. Jesus faced the Pharisees.

'Why are you concerned with the company I keep?' he demanded of them. 'I have not come to call the righteous but sinners to change their ways. It is not the healthy who need a doctor, but those who are sick. These men and women who eat and drink with me, *you* have rejected from your synagogues. If you could, you would shut the Kingdom of Heaven against them because you do not know the way yourselves. . . .'

The Pharisee came forward, filled with righteous anger. 'We know what is lawful and what is not,' he said. 'You and your disciples break the law. Healing on the Sabbath, claiming to forgive sins, eating with unwashed hands, mingling with outcasts . . . !'

Jesus' voice was quiet as he answered them. 'If you knew the meaning of God's words, "I will have mercy and not sacrifice," you would not have condemned the innocent.' And as he spoke he looked tenderly down at the little girl.

Andrew was still troubled, and said softly, 'He asked why we don't fast as we did with the Baptist, master.'

Looking round the guests, and then at John, Jesus said, 'This is a marriage feast. Would you have the friends of the bridegroom mourn while the bridegroom is with them?'

There was a burst of laughter and Jesus added almost to himself, 'But a time will come when the bridegroom is taken from them. That is the time. Those are the days when they will fast.'

Suddenly saddened, John asked, 'What do you mean, master?' But Jesus had become aware of the man from Kerioth staring at him. 'You wanted me, friend?' he asked. The man explained that he and his friend Thomas had brought a message from Jesus' kinsman, John the Baptist of Judea.

'From John?' asked Jesus eagerly, 'from prison . . . ?'

'Yes,' said Thomas, 'from prison. He sent us to ask—' but the other interrupted him hastily, saying, 'Understand, sir, that we are only messengers. For myself, since I have been in Galilee I have seen things and heard tales that leave me in no doubt. But John is a prisoner, and you know how it is when a man is shut up. Things prey on his mind.'

'What did John ask?' asked Jesus, and the stranger, looking straight at him, put the question: 'Are you he that shall come— or must we look for another?'

There was a murmur from the crowd of people gathered around, and the scribe and Pharisee drew nearer. The murmur died away to an expectant hush before Jesus spoke again.

'Go and tell John the things that you have seen and heard. How the blind receive their sight, the lame walk, the deaf hear, and say, "The poor have the good tidings preached to them."'

But Thomas was not satisfied with his reply. 'But *are* you he?' he persisted. 'We must have an answer.' But his friend checked him.

'We have our answer, Thomas. We'll go and tell John.'

Then he turned to Jesus and his voice was charged with excitement. 'And I shall come back—master.'

Jesus smiled at him. 'What is your name, friend?'

'Judas Iscariot.'

The Pharisee was not satisfied with all that he had heard.

'If you claim to be the one John heralded,' he said, 'give us a sign.'

Jesus answered him patiently. 'Can you not read the signs of the times?' he asked. 'In the evening you say, "To-morrow it will be fine, the sky is red" and in the morning, "A stormy day, the sky is red and angry." You, who can tell the weather by looking at the sky, with all your learning, cannot read the signs of the times so plainly given you. God sent John the Baptist, and no man has been greater than he. Those thousands of people who accepted baptism by John—and they included tax gatherers—were carrying out God's purpose, proving the wisdom of his ways.'

'He was a madman,' interrupted the scribe.

'But you Pharisees and lawyers thought you knew better,' Jesus went on, ignoring the interruption. 'You thought you must call the tune yourself like children playing in the market place calling out, "We piped and you did not dance. We sang your dirges and you did not weep."'

This was something the crowd could understand, and they all laughed, remembering their childhood games.

'And see what perverse children you are!' Jesus persisted. 'For John the Baptist came eating no bread and drinking no wine, and you say he is a madman. Then comes the Son of Man eating and drinking, and you say, "Look at that glutton, that drinker—a friend of tax collectors and outcasts!"' There was more laughter and as the people repeated the joke to each other Jesus added, 'And yet, God's ways have been proved wise by His children over and over again.'

There was a sudden commotion at the door, and a voice could be heard crying, 'Let me through. Let me through.' The crowd round the door drew back and a richly dressed man burst into the room, calling out, 'Is Jesus of Nazareth in here?'

Simon murmured a warning to Jesus. 'Here's more trouble, master,' he said. 'He's one of the rulers of the synagogue.'

'Probably come to complain about healing the poor lunatic on the Sabbath,' said John and they rose and stood in front of Jesus ready to protect him.

At once the Pharisee recognized the man.

'Jairus—Jairus, my friend, what is the matter?' he demanded; but Jairus took no heed of him.

'Where is Jesus, where is Jesus?' he asked.

Jesus came forward. 'I am here, friend.'

To everyone's astonishment Jairus, a ruler of the synagogue, threw himself down at Jesus' feet. Brokenly he cried, 'Jesus, rabbi. I beg you to come with me. My little daughter, my only child, is dying—I pray you to come and lay your hands on her that she may live.'

Jesus put a firm hand on his shoulder. 'Take me to her,' he said.

The crowd made way for them and Jairus led the way out of the narrow street. Jesus and the disciples hurried to keep up with him and again a large crowd followed. They were still some way from Jairus' house when a young man came running towards them. Fear gripped Jairus as he recognized the youth as one of his own servants. When he reached his master he fell on his knees crying. 'Sir, she is dead. Your daughter is dead. No use to bring the rabbi now.' Jairus covered his face with his hands, and the crowd waited, hushed and tense as in the distance came the sound of a wailing lament.

Jesus spoke to Jairus gently, 'Don't be afraid,' he said. 'Go on believing.' Then as Jairus hastened to his home Jesus turned to his disciples and the crowd. 'Simon, James and John, follow me,' he said. 'The rest of you stay here.'

The sound of wailing grew louder, and it was easy to know Jairus' house by the crowd that waited at the door. Jesus and the three disciples entered the house.

On a bed a little girl was lying, pale and still, while her mother and other female relations stood round her, weeping. Round about the door a group of people stood, wailing for the dead, while a flute player played a mournful funeral dirge.

Jairus stood by the door waiting for Jesus. He was trying to hold on to his faith, and looked to Jesus with an almost despairing hope.

Jesus held up a hand to hush the mourners. 'Why are you making all this noise?' he asked. 'The child is not dead but sleeping.' The remark was greeted with bitter laughter.

'Go back to your work,' said Jesus. Reluctantly, the mourners left the room, while Jesus crossed to the bed, and looked down tenderly at the little girl. Jairus went to his wife and put his arm around her.

'It's too late,' she sobbed, 'too late.' But Jairus hushed her, urging her only to have faith. Jesus sat down on the bed, and took the little girl's hand firmly in his own.

'Little girl,' he said, 'it's time to get up.'

Breathless, the mother and father waited. Slowly the little girl's eyes opened. She looked first at Jesus and smiled; then she looked at her mother and father. She sat up, glanced round the room, then put her feet to the ground and stood up. At this the mother rushed to her child, holding her tightly and weeping over her—laughing too for joy, and murmuring, 'My darling, my lamb, my precious child.'

'I'm hungry,' said the little girl. Jairus fell on his knees beside Jesus and cried, 'Master, master, what can I say?'

'See that you tell no one what has happened,' said Jesus, and then with a smile, 'and give the little girl something to eat.'

Without waiting for further thanks, he left the house with Simon, James and John, while the little girl ran to the door to wave after them.

After this, Jesus left the town and went around the whole of Galilee telling people about the Kingdom of God, and curing every sort of illness among the people; and his fame spread through the whole land.

PART 4

Jesus the Teacher

WHEREVER Jesus went he was followed by crowds. People from Galilee, from Judea, even from Tyre and Sidon and other countries farther afield who had heard all he was doing came many miles to join him; and his way of teaching filled them with amazement for he taught like one having authority and yet not like the scribes.

One Sabbath day Jesus was sitting teaching in a synagogue. Among his listeners were the four fishermen, Simon and his brother Andrew, and James and John whom Jesus had nicknamed the 'Sons of Thunder,' and the publican, Levi whom Jesus called 'Matthew' which means 'Gift of God.' There were others too who had become disciples of Jesus; Judas Iscariot, his dark face alive with intelligence, Thomas Didymus, frowning and a little mystified, Philip the farmer and his friend Nathaniel Bartholomew. And as always, wherever Jesus taught, there were scribes and Pharisees who listened as intently as the rest but with a certain suspicion.

Suddenly, a man who had been squatting on the outskirts of the group rose quietly, and with some difficulty began to edge his way to the front. His right arm which hung limp and useless by his side brushed against one of the Pharisees as he tried to make his way through the crowd towards Jesus. The Pharisee guessed his intention and followed him.

When the man reached the front of the crowd his courage seemed to fail him and he squatted down with the others. But Jesus had seen him.

'My friend,' said Jesus gently, 'stand up and come to me.'

The man struggled to his feet, and came forward. Jesus held out his hands to him, and the man put his left hand in his, saying as he did so, 'Sir, my right arm is useless. One day I was lifting a heavy stone and it fell and crushed my hand. It's withered now, sir.'

'What do you want me to do?' asked Jesus.

The man's rough voice was eager as he replied, 'Sir, I am a stonemason. I make a living by my hands. Heal me, Jesus. I'm ashamed to beg.'

There was immediate protest from some of those nearby.

'Scandalous,' muttered the Pharisee, 'the man should know better.' And a scribe, voicing the thoughts of many, said, 'It is unlawful to heal on the Sabbath. Surely the rabbi will not cure him.'

Jesus looked at them in silence for a moment, angry at their narrowness of mind and hardness of heart. Then he said, 'I will ask you a question. Is it lawful on the Sabbath day to do good or to do harm by leaving the good undone?'

There was no answer.

'Is it right to save life or to destroy it? Who among you,' he went on, while the Pharisee and the scribe watched him narrowly, 'if one of his sheep were to fall into a pit on the Sabbath day, would not lift it out?'

Many smiled in agreement with this; but the Pharisees watched him in stubborn silence, as he went on, 'Is not a man of more value than a sheep?'

Turning to the man and speaking gently but with great authority, Jesus said: 'Hold out your hand.'

The silence was intense. The disciples watched with growing excitement, and only Judas, who foresaw trouble, looked anxious, as the man, with his eyes fixed on Jesus, slowly raised his arm. He stared at his hand speechless, as the fingers that had been useless moved. He clenched and unclenched his fist and then, almost crying in his gratitude, he bent and kissed Jesus' hands.

The people crowded round, talking excitedly, and examining the hand that had been healed, while the man cried over and over again, 'Praise God, my hand is of use to me again. I'll be back at work to-morrow.'

As the disciples followed Jesus out of the synagogue the Pharisee went up to the stonemason.

'You will be reported for this Sabbath-breaking,' he said, 'and very likely excommunicated from the synagogue.'

The man grinned. 'That won't stop me praising God or following after Jesus,' he said.

'Enough of this impudence,' said the Pharisee. 'Go to your home.' And the man went off cheerfully, calling out, 'Yes, and to work to-morrow.'

The Pharisee and the scribe were left alone, and spoke in lowered voices.

'Galilee of the Gentiles,' said the scribe. 'It is well named. It would take little to sway these Galileans from the religion of their forefathers.'

'What can you expect,' asked the Pharisee, 'when King Herod himself is false to our faith and is like a puppet in the hands of pagan Rome?'

The scribe questioned whether even Herod would dare to disregard a charge of Sabbath-breaking; and his companion asked who would report it to him. 'You are not suggesting, I hope, that a Pharisee go begging to King Herod?'

'If it would mean the arrest of Jesus of Nazareth,' said the scribe, 'we should stop at nothing. . . . Remember, it was Herod who put John the Baptist to death. Already he is suspicious of Jesus, fearing that he may be the Baptist risen from the dead. Ridiculous, I know,' he said, as the Pharisee laughed scornfully, 'but a charge of Sabbath-breaking brought against Jesus would give him an excuse to arrest.'

'And the penalty may well be death?' asked the Pharisee. The scribe nodded. 'My friend, you have convinced me. Distasteful as the matter is, I see where my duty lies.'

After Jesus left the synagogue he went to the top of a hill above the lake of Galilee. He looked down on the town of Capernaum below him; then he knelt to pray.

Wherever Jesus went he was followed by crowds

Teaching in the synagogue

Healing on the Sabbath

Many people had followed him, and would have gone up to join him, but John stopped them, saying that Jesus would sooner be alone to pray. They began to talk of the day's happenings, and Matthew laughed as he recalled the stir Jesus had made in the synagogue. Only Judas was grave, wondering if it had been wise to anger the Pharisees.

But Matthew refused to have his gaiety dampened. 'Oh,' he said cheerfully, 'they let anything anger them. Remember how they went for the master in my house?' He gave a fair imitation of the Pharisee's voice and manner as he said, ' "Eating with publicans and sinners!" '

Judas found it hard to share Matthew's cheerful optimism. The Pharisees, he pointed out, were the religious leaders, and it wouldn't do to disregard all their teaching. He was backed up by Thomas Didymus. He had great faith in Jesus, he said, but he doubted the wisdom of some of his actions.

Simon urged him not to doubt, but to believe, and he said that he and his brother had left all to follow Jesus. Others had gathered round, and they echoed this. Philip recalled how, when he had asked if he could go and bid his people good-bye, Jesus had said, 'Philip, you have put your hand to a different sort of plough now. You must keep your furrow straight and not look back.' The young scholar Nathaniel told Thomas that he too had doubted at first. 'Can any good thing come out of Nazareth?' he had asked when Philip had told him of Jesus.

'But when I saw him,' said Nathaniel, 'it was as though the scriptures I had been reading had come to life and the Heavens had opened.'

'Some say this Jesus is the promised King of Israel.' The speaker was a wild-looking young man who wore a knife in his belt. 'If so he'll find plenty of support from the knife-men.' The 'knife-men' or 'Zealots' were a band of men who had vowed to drive the Romans out of Israel.

Two other men, Thaddeus and James Alphaeus, joined the group and they all sat down on the ground to wait for Jesus.

Above them on the hillside Jesus was praying for his disciples, and having prayed he came down the hill to join them.

'Peace be unto you, little flock,' he said, and in their different ways they greeted him in return.

'My friends,' said Jesus, 'many of you have left your homes to follow me as sheep follow their shepherd, because you know that I bring you the good tidings of God's Kingdom. Some of you I have called from your work and you have come. Simon and Andrew from their nets, and also James and John, the sons of Zebedee; Matthew from his seat of custom, Philip from his plough, and Nathaniel Bartholomew from his books. Now the time has come for me to call more. To appoint twelve "apostles" to be with me and later to be sent out to spread the good news of the Kingdom and to heal the sick.' There was an expectant silence as Jesus looked around the little crowd of men.

'These are the men I call to join the company of apostles.' He named them: Thomas Didymus, James, son of Alphaeus, Thaddeus, Simon the Zealot and Judas Iscariot. Judas sprang to his feet and came over to Jesus in great excitement.

'Master, you've chosen *me?*'

'Why not, Judas?' asked Jesus.

'I'm a southerner,' answered Judas, still unable to believe his good fortune, 'not a native of Galilee like the others. I dared not hope that you'd choose me.'

Jesus told him that his mission was not only to Galilee.

'To Jerusalem?' asked Judas eagerly.

'To the whole world.'

The disciples asked how they were to have the authority to teach or the power to heal, and Jesus told them to pray and all that was needed would be given.

'Lord, teach us to pray,' said John.

So Jesus taught them a new prayer. 'When you pray,' he said, 'say: "Our Father who art in Heaven, hallowed be Thy name. Thy Kingdom come. Thy will be done on earth as it is in Heaven. Give us this day our daily bread and forgive us our debts as we forgive our debtors, and lead us not into temptation, but deliver us from evil."'

Eagerly, prompting each other when they forgot, they repeated the prayer.

Soon after this Jesus and his twelve disciples set out across the hills to go to Nazareth, where he had been brought up; and when they reached the town they went to see Mary, his mother, and she met his disciples, some of them for the first time. She never tired of hearing what they told her about her son: of his power to move men, and how they followed him.

'Does he get very tired?' asked Mary anxiously.

'No,' said Simon, 'he doesn't get tired exactly. Only when there's been a lot of healing. Then he says he "feels the power go out of him." I reckon it's like his own strong nature going out of him into those poor sick ones.'

'You only have to be near him,' chimed in Matthew, 'to feel that power. Look at me. I wasn't sick, only sinful as you might say.' He laughed at himself, as he was always ready to do. 'But I felt it. Just as if I was made a whole complete man for the first time ever.'

'And you twelve are going to help him with his work?' asked Mary.

'Yes,' said John. 'He says we can have the power to heal too. Won't it be wonderful? To be able to go out and say, "In the name of Jesus of Nazareth, take up your bed and walk!"'

Mary repeated it softly to herself: '"In the name of Jesus of Nazareth"—my son.'

Matthew broke the silence with his usual gaiety. 'He says he's going to send us out on our own to heal. Fancy me, a tax collector—healing and teaching!'

But Judas struck a serious note, saying he thought they should not leave Jesus, and that he was afraid for him: that although people flocked to him and even those who had turned their backs on religion before listened to him, there was danger because his way of teaching was different.

Mary pressed them to know what danger there could be.

'What do you think,' asked Judas, 'the priests and the Pharisees and the rulers of the synagogue think of him? And Herod who imprisoned John? What is the Roman Governor going to do when he learns that thousands are following Jesus of Nazareth? These are the powerful ones—the ones who could harm him.'

Mary protested that Jesus did not go against them—that indeed he taught in the synagogues, and Matthew hastened to comfort Mary, telling her of the Roman centurion whose servant Jesus had healed, and Jairus, a ruler of the synagogue, who had been on his knees to Jesus.

'Don't let Judas scare you, lady,' he ended; 'he's a southerner, you know, and always a bit of a pessimist.' Judas replied tersely that it was in the south that the power and danger lay.

But Mary had had enough of worry and fear. Nothing, she said, could make her afraid on this day, with her son home, in his own town, with his family and friends; and as if to bring them back to the safe everyday world, a small boy ran in from the carpenter's shop followed by Jesus.

'I say,' said the boy, 'what do you think? Jesus has told me how to finish off that yoke. But he won't do it for me to-day because it's the Sabbath.'

'I should think not indeed,' said Mary. The boy gave a mischievous look at Jesus.

'But you *do* do things on the Sabbath, don't you?' he said. '*I* know.'

Jesus laughed. 'What do you know, Joses?' he asked.

'You heal and help people,' said the boy. ' "The Sabbath was made for man, not man for the Sabbath." *You* said that.'

'And I mean it,' said Jesus.

'Well, then,' persisted Joses, 'why couldn't you help me with that yoke?'

'Because,' said Jesus, 'that is an everyday job and can wait for to-morrow. If your donkey had fallen into a pit I would help you rescue him. If we were in the desert we would hunt for food and prepare it.'

'On the Sabbath?' queried the boy.

'Of course. Because these things would be necessary and could not wait. God gave us the Sabbath day to rest and to worship. But He gave us good sense too.'

'I see,' said Joses, thoughtfully. Then he asked impulsively, 'May I sit next to you in the synagogue?'

'Of course,' said Jesus, but Mary felt the boy was asking too much and said, 'You must be a good boy, and not bother Jesus. He won't be sitting with you all the time. He will be with the rabbis.' She lifted her head proudly, as she added, 'Reading the lesson and giving the address too, I expect.'

Taking his mother by one hand, and Joses by the other, Jesus left the house, and followed by the disciples walked through the streets to the synagogue as he had done so often as a boy.

There Mary joined the women in a separate gallery. Jesus was with the disciples and Joses sat on the ground near the raised stand from which the words of the law and the prophets were read. Joses listened intently, as an elder read from the book of Exodus:

'Remember the Sabbath day to keep it holy. Six days shalt thou labour and do all thy work. But the seventh day is a Sabbath unto the Lord thy God. In it thou shalt do no manner of work, nor thy son, nor thy daughter, thy manservant nor thy maidservant, thy cattle nor the stranger that is within thy gates. For in six days the Lord made heaven and earth, the sea and all that in them is, and rested the seventh day. Wherefore the Lord blessed the seventh day and hallowed it.'

Joses looked up at Jesus and gave an understanding grin.

After the tenth and last commandment the elder rolled up the scroll, and handed it to an attendant. Jesus and the other young men near him were now on their feet, each of them prepared to read the second lesson which was from the prophets.

'This is the law of God,' said the elder. 'Hear now the word of the prophet Isaiah.' He stepped down from the reading stand. The attendant handed another scroll to Jesus, who took the elder's place and began to read:

'The spirit of the Lord is upon me, because he appointed me to preach good tidings to the poor. He sent me to proclaim release to the captives. And new eyes for the blind. To set at liberty those that are bruised. To proclaim the acceptable year of the Lord.'

Then Jesus rolled up the scroll, sat down and began his discourse.

'To-day, in your very hearing,' he said, 'this text is coming true.' There was a gasp of surprise and an interested murmur from the congregation. 'The Kingdom of God is very near and I have come to give the good tidings to you and to other cities also. For this was I sent.'

'Sent? By whom?' asked the elder sharply; and the other elders leaned forward, alert to possible blasphemy.

'By our Father in Heaven,' said Jesus, and again there was a murmur from the people.

'Isn't this Jesus, the carpenter?' muttered one elder to another, who told him yes, this was Jesus, son of Joseph; while up in the women's gallery Mary heard all around her the same query.

'Does he mean Joseph,' asked one woman, 'when he speaks of his "Father in Heaven"?' Mary shook her head.

'You say,' the first elder asked Jesus, choosing his words with care, 'you say the Kingdom of God is very near. Is it here in Nazareth?'

'Here and in all places where I shall go,' replied Jesus.

'Where you shall go, Jesus?' said another elder sternly. 'Are you suggesting that you are a prophet sent by God?'

Jesus was silent, and the first elder continued, 'Whatever "good tidings" you have, let us hear them, but remember, we know the law and we have before us the words of the Holy Prophets.'

'I have not come to abolish the law or the prophets,' said Jesus. 'I have come to fulfil them. The man who teaches people to forget one of these commandments shall count for little in the Kingdom of Heaven.'

The elders seemed relieved; but Jesus astonished them with his next words.

'But believe me,' he said, 'if you do no better than the lawyers and Pharisees in your *observance* of the law, you shall certainly not enter the Kingdom.'

An amused murmur ran through the congregation, and the elders were uneasy again.

'You have heard to-day,' went on Jesus, 'the commandment "Thou shalt do no murder," and you know that murderers are punished by law. I tell you, that anyone who is angry with his brother, who slanders his neighbour, or calls another man a fool is guilty in God's eyes. You have heard that it is lawful to measure your revenge—an eye for an eye and a tooth for a tooth; but I say to you, repay evil with *good*. If anyone strikes you on the right cheek, turn to him the left also. Give to the man that asks you, and from one who wants to borrow, do not turn away. Love your enemies and be merciful even as your Father is merciful. This way you will spread the good tidings to the poor. You will set free those who are imprisoned by worldly cares. You will give new eyes to the blind. You will be heralds of God's Kingdom.'

He rose as he finished speaking, and at once there was a murmur of approval from the people. They thought he spoke well, and those

He went to the top of a hill above the lake of Galilee

In the synagogue at Nazareth

Jesus and the Twelve

who did not know him asked others who he was. Those who knew him and his family marvelled that a carpenter's son should speak so well and so freely.

But the elder rose, his face heavy with disapproval.

'Jesus, son of Joseph,' he spoke with authority and the people grew quiet. 'Word has reached us of the work you have been doing in Capernaum, and your fellow townsmen had doubtless hoped to see some "wonder" performed here in Nazareth.' He paused to let these words have their effect. 'I understand they have been disappointed.' There was a murmur of agreement. 'But we of the synagogue do not ask for "miracles," ' he continued, 'we were merely interested to hear you speak and for this reason you were invited to read the lesson and expound upon it if you wished. This is a privilege awarded to many young men of learning. But you have abused that privilege,' his voice rose as his anger increased. 'You have taken upon yourself to put new interpretations on our law, to criticize the teachers and lawyers and to claim that you have been sent from God. Take care, young man, that you do not find yourself guilty of blasphemy.'

Jesus heard him in silence, and then said quietly,

'Truly, has Isaiah prophesied of you hypocrites.' There was a gasp from the people. Jesus took the scroll of Isaiah from the attendant and read the passage: ' "These people honour me with their lips, but their hearts are far from me." '

The elder nearly choked with anger. 'Don't dare to quote the scriptures against us,' he said.

'You search the scriptures,' replied Jesus, 'thinking to find eternal life in them. But those very scriptures are my witnesses.'

Immediately there was protest from the crowd, and a hubbub broke out. One man called out that that kind of talk might be all right in Capernaum, but that he couldn't fool his own people so easily. Others told him jeeringly to go back to his carpentering, and many asked him for a sign to prove he was a prophet. 'Cure yourself, doctor,' they yelled, growing bolder. But Jesus hushed them with upraised hand.

'Indeed, I say to you,' he said calmly, 'no prophet is accepted in his own country.' He reminded them how in Elijah's day there was

famine in Israel and yet Elijah was not sent to help a single one of
them, although he *was* sent to a city of Sidon; and how, in the
prophet Elisha's time, there had been many lepers in Israel, not
one of whom was cured, but Naaman, a Syrian, was cured.

There were angry murmurs from the crowd and the elder warned
Jesus again not to quote instances from the scriptures to justify what
he called his 'blasphemies.'

But to the second elder this was the final insult. He rose and ad-
dressed the people. 'This carpenter,' he said, 'whom we have
known for thirty years, has set himself up as a prophet. He has no
witness. He gives no sign. And because we challenge him he dares
to reproach us: to speak of us, his countrymen and kinsfolk, as of
less account than Gentiles and lepers.' His voice rose, 'Are we
going to hear this from Jesus, the carpenter?'

At once the people responded, with cries of 'blasphemer,' 'here-
tic,' 'false prophet.' Some demanded that he should be banished
from the synagogue, and others shouted that he should be taken to
the cliff—to be thrown down to his death; and the elders acquiesced.

Two of the young men went to seize him, but Jesus of his own ac-
cord quietly descended from the platform and walked through the
synagogue. The angry crowd followed, shaking their fists and shouting. Simon and John managed to get close to him, but the rest of
the disciples were cut off. His mother watched in distress from the
women's gallery, then turned and hurried down the steps and out
of the building.

Jesus walked on with firm step, the crowd surging round him,
still shouting and threatening. By now they had become a dis-
orderly mob, filled with blind hatred, out of hand, ruthless, as they
drove him to the top of the hill whereon their city was built.

To the very top of a steep cliff they drove him and for a moment
Jesus looked down at the valley and the jagged rocks below. Then
he turned to face the shouting mob with a look of searching pity.
This was the moment when they should have seized him and
thrown him over, but under his gaze they suddenly grew quiet and
those nearest to him drew back, each man reluctant to be the first
to lay hands on him. Quietly Jesus walked through the midst
of them and went his way.

So Jesus left Nazareth because the people there had no faith.

On the hillside overlooking Lake Galilee Jesus prayed alone. 'Father, the time has come when I must send out those that you gave me to teach and to heal and to spread the good tidings of Thy Kingdom. Be with them, Father, for I send them out like sheep among wolves. Guard them and guide them and deliver them from evil. For Thine is the Kingdom, and the power and the glory.'

Here, on the hillside, the disciples found him. They were ashamed and distressed at having, as they felt, failed him in the synagogue. 'There we were in Nazareth,' said Simon, 'all twelve of us, and yet we couldn't quieten that angry crowd. It seems we aren't much help to you. You don't really need us.'

'The Kingdom needs you, Simon,' said Jesus. 'Have you forgotten that you are to be a fisher of men?'

Just then John came running up with Judas, saying that people from all the villages around were searching for him because they thought he had gone away. They were scattering all over the place, not knowing which way to go.

'Like sheep without a shepherd,' said Jesus, and Judas commented, 'More like ripe corn ready for the cutting.' Jesus said he was right, that the harvest was plentiful, but the labourers were few.

Simon was puzzled by this talk of fishers, shepherds and harvest. 'You and Judas talk in riddles, master,' he said.

'But about one thing, Simon,' replied Jesus: 'the Kingdom of God. You twelve are the fishers, the shepherds, the harvest labourers who will bring God's children to His Kingdom.'

When Simon protested that it was Jesus the people wanted, not the disciples, Jesus replied that he who listened to them, listened to him. 'For I have chosen you to do my Father's work,' he said. 'He that rejects you rejects me and Him that sent me.'

'The master said we were to go out in his name, Simon,' said John, 'to teach and to heal. Didn't you, master?'

'Yes, John,' replied Jesus. 'And the time has come for you to go. Sit down and I will tell you.'

They sat on the ground in a circle round him. 'You will travel two and two together,' he said, 'not yet into the pagan countries, not even to Samaria, but to the cities and villages of Galilee and Judea, to the lost sheep of the House of Israel. Do as you have seen me do. Spread the good news of the Kingdom, heal the sick, raise the dead, speak in the daylight the things I tell you in the dark. And the things you hear in whispers proclaim on the housetops. Give freely because you have received freely. Take no money nor knapsack for the journey, nor even a change of clothes or staff for the road. For the labourer is worthy of his keep!'

It was the practical Matthew who voiced their feelings: 'But without money where shall we stay, master?'

Wherever they might find themselves, Jesus told them. They were to find someone respected in the town or village, and stay with him, leaving their blessing on his house. If they were refused hospitality, they were to leave that house or that town, and shake the dust of it from their feet.

But James was still troubled. 'Master,' he said, 'no money, no food, no clothes, how can we do our work if we have to worry about these things?'

'You must not worry or even think about them, James,' said Jesus. 'Your Father in Heaven knows what you need. Look at the birds, they neither sow nor reap nor store away food into barns. Yet your heavenly Father feeds them. And, as for clothes, consider these lilies of the field,' he pointed to the brightly coloured anemones growing among the grass on the hillside. 'They neither toil nor spin, and yet Solomon in all his glory was not arrayed like one of these. Now, if God so clothes the flowers of the field which are alive to-day, and burnt with the grass to-morrow, is he not much more likely to clothe you?' and he smiled as he added, 'O, you of little faith.'

John hastened to the defence of his brother. 'James *has* faith, master,' he assured him. 'But he's always been the practical one of the family. Thinking for both of us.'

By now the disciples were on their feet, eagerly discussing what Jesus had said, and planning who should go with whom, since they were to go in pairs. Only Judas did not share their excitement, and once more he protested that it was dangerous for them to leave Jesus.

'Master,' begged Judas, 'do not send all your friends away. Let some of us stay with you.'

Jesus shook his head, smiling. 'But what of the "ripe corn ready for the cutting," Judas?' he asked. 'All the harvest labourers will be needed to gather it in.'

'But it is where *you* are that the harvest is richest, master,' protested Judas. 'And where there's a rich harvest there is danger—enemies who seek to steal and destroy because the harvest is not theirs.'

'If there is danger for me there is danger for all of you. For the disciple is not above his teacher and will fare no better. Believe me, they will scourge *you* in their synagogues and drag you into court and say all manner of evil things against you, falsely for my sake.'

When Judas protested that he was not afraid for himself, Jesus went on, 'No, you will rejoice and be glad for the Kingdom of God is yours.'

He paused for a moment, looking at them all intently, and choosing his words carefully; then he went on: 'There will be believers and unbelievers. Even in the same family you may find division, between a man and his father, between daughter and mother. When you find this division remember I have not come to bring peace but a sword.'

'A sword?' Judas' fears vanished. This was the leader Israel awaited: a militant messiah. He turned to Simon the Zealot with a look of triumph. Together they would rally an army of protectors for Jesus.

So the disciples went off two and two together, spreading the good news of the Kingdom of God, and healing all manner of sickness among the people.

PART 5

Jesus the King

W<small>HEN</small> the disciples returned to Jesus they told him everything about their mission: how they had taught and healed, and about the death of John the Baptist. And because they were tired, Jesus took them to a quiet place on the other side of the lake so that they could rest. But news of their coming quickly spread, and very soon multitudes followed them once more. Jesus would not send them away, but had compassion on them, teaching them many things and healing those that were sick.

The disciples were dog-tired and some of them were inclined to grumble.

'So much for our "rest in a quiet place," ' said Thomas, looking at the crowds around them. 'Why, it's been the busiest day we've had for months.'

'Look at them,' said Matthew. 'Thousands of them, and not a bite to eat all day like us.'

'If they're as hungry as I am,' added Philip, 'they'll be fainting before they get home. Most of them come from the other side of the lake.'

Nathaniel suggested that Philip should tell Jesus this; so Philip went to him, saying it was nearly sundown, and asking whether it would not be best to send the people away, so that they could get something to eat at the farms and villages nearby. But Jesus said there was no need to send them away. 'Feed them yourselves,' he said.

'Why, master,' said Philip, 'we haven't the money to buy food for all these people. There's about five thousand.'

'What food have you got with you?' asked Jesus, and Philip told him that they had only enough for themselves.

'There's a boy here with some bread and fish,' said Andrew. 'Can we buy them, son?'

The boy nodded, and Andrew looked in his basket to see how many he had.

'Five barley loaves and two dried fish,' reported Andrew with a laugh. 'What good is that among so many?'

'Tell the people to sit down,' said Jesus.

'Master,' said Simon in dismay, 'if we do that they'll think we have food for them.'

But the boy was quite confident. 'You're going to feed them with my bread and fish, aren't you?' he asked; and Jesus asked Simon where was his faith.

'I'm sorry, master,' said Simon, and at once turned to the others with instructions. Andrew was to tell one section of the crowd; John was to run and tell those over by the rocks, and 'James, you Son of Thunder,' he went on, 'your voice is loud enough, see how many you can reach.'

'What shall I say?' asked James.

'Just tell them to sit down on the grass,' said Simon, and when James looked doubtful, he added briskly, 'Go on, James, it's the master's order.'

So off went James, and a moment later his booming voice could be heard telling the people that the master wanted them all to sit down on the grass just where they were. And all over the hillside, the other disciples were repeating the same request.

Men, women and children settled themselves on the ground, all looking expectantly towards Jesus and the disciples.

The boy with the basket of bread and fish stood beside Jesus. When the disciples returned he took the bread and broke it into pieces, saying the familiar blessing, 'Thanks be to Thee, O God, King of the world, who bringest forth bread from the earth.' Then, taking the basket from the boy, he added, 'Father we thank Thee for giving us our daily bread. Grant that Thy hungry children may be filled, not only with the bread that perishes but with the true bread of Heaven that gives life to the world. Amen.'

He handed the basket of bread to John, telling him to give to everyone as much as he wanted, and told the other disciples to go with him and help him.

'But, master,' protested Thomas, 'we have no food to give them.'

'Then take your empty baskets,' said Jesus, and with doubt and uncertainty the disciples followed. Judas hesitated for a moment and half turned back to Jesus, but then he too followed the others.

They shared the bread and fish from the boy's basket and went to different parts of the crowd. Everywhere families and friends settled down to enjoy the meal, and eager hands were stretched to the baskets as they were offered to them. Fathers took enough to divide up for their children, and friends shared their portions with each other. Right through the crowd on the hillside the disciples went, until all the five thousand had been fed and were satisfied; and when all had finished they were able to gather up enough fragments to fill twelve baskets, which they carried to Jesus.

There were murmurs of wonder and approval from the people. 'Manna from heaven,' some called the food.

'This man is a prophet sent from God,' called one man, fervently. 'As Elisha fed a hundred men with twenty loaves, so this man feeds five thousand with still less.'

One by one those around him echoed his words, saying that Jesus was the leader Israel had been waiting for, that he was the Messiah, the Redeemer of Israel, the King of the Jews. Soon their enthusiasm mounted, and the whole hillside was cheering and shouting with cries of 'Elijah,' 'Prophet,' 'Saviour,' 'Redeemer,' 'King.'

Judas, who was a man who liked action and to see results from what he did, was triumphantly excited.

'Master,' he cried, 'listen to them. The hungry people you have fed.'

But Jesus, recalling his temptation in the wilderness, answered, 'Man shall not live by bread alone.'

Judas was not to be daunted. 'At last you've fulfilled the prophecy, master,' he said urgently. 'They're calling you Saviour—Messiah—Redeemer of Israel. Truly you have reaped your harvest to-day. This is the proof the people awaited. The proof that you were sent from God.'

Once more Jesus quoted the scriptures in reply: 'Thou shalt not put the Lord thy God to the proof.'

But still Judas was not to be discouraged. 'Five thousand of them,' he said, his voice rising in his excitement, 'hailing you as their King. Enough to start a revolution—with the Passover near—backed by the religious leaders and the Zealots and with thousands from Galilee and Judea paying homage to you. You could ride into Jerusalem as a King. Tell them—tell them you are their King.' He leaned towards Jesus, his eyes shining with enthusiasm for his ambitious plans.

Jesus closed his eyes, and speaking almost to himself said resolutely, 'Thou shalt pay homage to the Lord Thy God and Him only shalt thou serve.'

Judas stepped back as if he had had a blow in the face from his beloved master. He stared, uncomprehending, as Jesus turned from him and walked away, and the crowd still cheered and acclaimed him. Then, still puzzled and indignant, he joined the other disciples, and soon they left the hillside and followed Jesus from the place.

They journeyed on, and in due course came to the country near Caesarea Philippi, and here among the hills they sat to rest for a while. But Jesus would not rest. He left them and went apart to pray.

The disciples sat, or lay on the ground, eating bread or sleeping a little, and presently they began to talk about the Kingdom. John said he felt it was drawing very near, and Simon said he felt the Kingdom closest when the master had walked over stormy waters to their boat.

'It seemed,' he said, 'as if I saw how God meant us to be in his own image and having dominion over the earth and the sea. That's why I called out, "Master, if it be you, bid me come and I will walk to you on the water." He smiled and said, "Come on then." And I did walk.' He faltered a little in the telling, and then added ruefully, 'but I didn't last for long.'

Matthew thought it tactful to change the subject. 'I thought the Kingdom had come all right,' he said, 'the other day when the master fed all those people and they stood and roared out that he was the King. That was exciting, that was.'

It was a bitter reminder for Judas. 'Yes,' he said savagely, 'but

what became of it? He spoiled it. He lost the chance. Just when the
people were united, ready to make him King—what did he do?'

'We don't know what he did, Judas,' replied Simon quietly, 'because he sent us away.'

'I'll tell you what he did,' said Judas, growing more heated. 'He
let it go to his head. . . .'

John leapt to his feet. 'You're mad, Judas. How dare you say
such a thing of the master?'

With a laugh, Matthew tried to pour oil on troubled waters.

'You don't know what you are talking about, Judas,' he said.
'First you grumble because the master didn't take the chance to be
King, and now you say "he let it go to his head." You can't have
it both ways, you know.'

'I know what I'm talking about,' retorted Judas, 'and I'm not
going against the master, John. I love him as much as any of you,
and I'd tell him what I think to his face.'

'Well, what do you think?' asked Simon.

'I think he's deliberately running himself into danger,' said Judas.
'Deliberately turning his back on the right kind of support, just
when it is within reach. He's let the idea take hold of him that he
and his little band of twelve can establish the Kingdom *alone,* and
that the only way into the Kingdom is "through him" in some
mysterious way. I don't know what he means, and I don't know
why he's doing it, but to me the Kingdom seems farther away than
ever now.'

Simon urged him not to lose his faith, not to be like him when
the master had bidden him to walk to him on the water: confident
at first while he looked towards Jesus, but afraid as soon as he
looked away.

While he spoke Jesus himself had joined them and stood, unheeded for the moment, listening to what they said. He heard
Thomas declare that there was something in what Judas had said,
and that they were losing their followers—not just the hysterical
crowds, but the regular followers, some of them rich folk and
Pharisees.

'And that band of Zealots I brought from Judea,' added Judas.

'That's right,' said Thomas. 'You don't see any of them around
now. There's many's deserted him.'

Jesus stepped forward into their midst. 'And you, little flock,' he asked, 'are you also wanting to go away?'

Judas and Thomas were startled, and silent, but Simon spoke up instantly: 'Lord, not us. To whom would we go?'

Jesus put his hand on Simon's shoulder, and asked what they had been speaking of. They told him they had been talking about the Kingdom, and some of them felt it was very near.

'It is,' said Jesus. 'Very near.'

'When, master, when shall we see it?' asked James.

'James,' Jesus reproached him, 'do you not understand yet that my Kingdom is not of this world?'

'Not of this world?' cried Judas, seizing on this. 'Shall we not see God's Kingdom in Israel then?'

'Let me ask you a question,' said Jesus. 'Whom do men say I am?'

'Some, like Herod,' replied Judas, 'say you are John the Baptist risen from the dead.'

Matthew added that he had heard the crowd calling out that Jesus was Elijah, and Thomas that most of the people thought he was one of the great prophets.

'But who do you say I am?' persisted Jesus.

It was Simon who answered, 'You are the Christ—the Son of the Living God.'

Jesus turned and looked at him, 'Simon bar Jonah, you are blessed indeed,' he said. 'Only my Father in Heaven could have made this truth known to you. From now on you shall be called Peter the Rock. On this rock I will build my church and the gates of Hell shall not prevail against it.'

'*Your* church?' muttered Judas to himself, and stood apart while all the other disciples fell on their knees around Jesus begging for his blessing, calling him 'Lord,' and 'Son of God.'

'See you tell nobody what has been made known to you,' said Jesus. 'For the Son of Man must go to Jerusalem, suffer much, be rejected by the chief priests and lawyers, be put to death,' there was a gasp from the disciples, and Jesus continued quietly, 'and on the third day be restored to life.'

The disciples looked at him, not comprehending. Simon Peter burst out, 'Heaven save you, Lord, this *shall* not happen to you!'

Again Jesus was reminded of his temptation. 'Get thee behind me, Satan,' he cried. Peter was deeply hurt, and protested: 'Lord!'

'Would you tempt me, Peter?' asked Jesus more gently. 'Would you put a stumbling block in my path? Now, your thoughts are of this world, not of God, for is it not written that the Son of Man is to be "despised and rejected of men; a man of sorrows and acquainted with grief"?'

'But, master!' protested Peter once more.

'You want me to save my life,' went on Jesus. 'He that wants to save his life shall lose it. He that is willing to lose his life for my sake and the sake of the good news shall save it.'

And now John pressed forward eagerly. 'Our lives are yours, master,' he said.

'He that would come after me,' said Jesus, 'must deny himself, take up his cross day by day and follow me.'

'Why do you speak of a cross?' asked Judas. 'We will bear anything for your sake, but a cross is a shameful thing for criminals to carry.'

Jesus looked directly at him. 'Indeed,' he said, 'if anyone is ashamed of me and my words, the Son of Man will be ashamed of him, when he comes in his Father's glory with the holy angels around him.'

Unable to bear the steady gaze of his eyes, Judas turned away, and went over to where Thomas and Simon the Zealot were talking together about Jesus' words. Thomas, doubtful as ever, wondered whether the Kingdom was coming with power and glory or with suffering and death, and Simon was troubled by what Jesus had said about being put to death. As Judas approached he turned and asked him what Jesus had meant.

Judas replied bitterly, 'I don't know. Everything seems to be slipping away from us. If only he'd listen—if only he'd listen to me instead of those ignorant fishermen. Peter, a rock on which he will build his church. *His* church! What does he mean?'

Six days later Jesus took Simon Peter, James and John, and they went alone up a very high mountain. When they had reached a great height, they paused, breathless from the climb, and looked back at the view below them.

'What a climb!' said Peter. 'My legs won't go any farther.'

Crossing Lake Galilee

'Do not be afraid'

Jesus and the epileptic boy

'But it's worth it,' said John. 'Look out there—the whole of Galilee stretched out before us. It's like being above the clouds.'

Peter asked if they could rest, and Jesus told them to do so, while he himself climbed a little higher. As they watched him go, James said that sometimes he felt they were not worthy of him, that they could never quite keep up with him, but always had to rest while he went on alone.

'He's gone to pray,' said John. 'To be alone with the Father. We can't hope to be as close to the Father as he is, James. I am beginning to see what he meant when he said, "I am the way, the truth and the life, no one comes to the Father but through me." It's as though he was the bridge between Heaven and earth.'

'Between Heaven and earth,' echoed James softly. 'Look up there, John, where the master's walking. It's like looking up into Heaven.'

The three of them, Peter, John and James, gazed up at the white figure of Jesus striding upwards against the dark mountainside, as though, John said almost to himself, he were going back to the Father. But Peter, overhearing him, said sharply, 'Don't say that. "Going back to the Father" sounds like death. It puts me in mind of what the master has been telling us so often these last days—how he is going to suffer and die and that in a little while we shall not see him.'

'I can't believe that he will ever die,' said John. 'I think he will be carried up to Heaven like Elijah.'

Peter answered him sharply. 'You "can't believe he will ever die"? Isn't that just what I said to the master and didn't he rebuke me: "Get thee behind me, Satan," he said, as though I were the devil tempting him. Peter the Rock, he called me, but sometimes I feel more like the shifting sand. You remember that story he told us about the man who built his house on the sand with no foundations under it? It was a fine house and stood up well until a storm broke over it and floods surged round it. Then it fell to the ground in ruins. In ruins. That's how I'd be if the master left us.'

'No, Peter,' John comforted him. 'Remember the wise man who dug deep down and laid the foundations of his house on the rock. Nothing could shake that house. Not the winds, nor the storms, nor the floods.' He paused for a moment, before he added, 'nor the gates of Hell.' Peter looked at him questioningly. 'Have you forgotten what the master said, Peter? "On this rock I will build my church and the gates of Hell will not prevail against it." '

'His church?' questioned James. 'What did he mean by that?'

With a flash of inspiration Peter answered: 'He meant the church of the Living God. The church of Christ.' He looked up towards Jesus. 'He meant that we on earth are to be like a solid rock of faith, even if—even *when* he goes back to his Father.'

As they watched Jesus, James said thoughtfully, 'Everything's changing, isn't it? Until now we looked to Moses and Elijah. The word of God came to us through them. But now we look to Jesus.'

'The word of God made flesh,' said John softly.

Suddenly the light on their upturned faces became brighter, till it was blinding in its intensity. They fell to their knees, and James, unable to bear it, shielded his eyes from the light with his arm.

But Peter faced the light unflinchingly, saying, almost in a whisper, 'Look—look at the master. Have the Heavens opened?'

'His face—his robe!' cried John in wonder.

On the mountain top Jesus stood bathed in the brilliant light: as he gazed upwards he seemed to be talking and listening.

'Who is he talking with?' asked James in wonder and Peter, almost in a whisper answered, 'With Moses and Elijah.'

James fell on his knees beside his brother. 'John,' he cried, 'I'm afraid to be here. It's holy ground.'

'It's good to be here,' Peter reassured him. 'If only the world could stay like this for ever. If only we could live on the mountain always.' And with a rush of happiness he called out to Jesus, 'Oh, master, let us make three shelters against the wind and the storm for you, for Moses and for Elijah.'

Even while he spoke the light began to fade, and darkness to fall. A mist rolled down the mountainside and there was a distant echo of thunder. James, in fear, clung to John, who stood still, listening. 'I can hear,' said John, 'I can hear the voice of God. "This is my beloved Son—listen to him." '

The mist cleared a little as they stood, and they waited silently until they saw Jesus returning to them. Then they fell on their knees, and when he came near James and John clung to his robe while Peter caught hold of his hand.

'Do not be afraid,' Jesus told them, and Peter cried out, 'Master, we saw . . .' and John, 'We heard. . . .' But Jesus interrupted them. 'Your eyes and ears were opened,' he said, 'so that you may better understand, but until the Son of Man has risen from the dead, tell no one what you have seen and heard to-day.'

While they were on their way down the mountain, the other nine disciples were standing at the corner of a street in the town below, surrounded by a crowd which, as usual, included some scribes. Judas stood with Thomas and Simon, and all looked very worried. A boy lay in a fit on the ground, and the disciples had failed to cure him, and, as Judas pointed out, their failure would raise doubts on all sides.

There was a sudden shriek from the boy, and his father, kneeling beside him, called out distractedly, 'Where is Jesus? Where is Jesus that he may cure my son?'

The child lay stiffly there, his back arched, his head tossing from side to side. Andrew knelt beside him, his hand on the boy's head, but he could do nothing.

'If only the master were here,' he said to Judas, 'or even Simon or John. They'd know what to do.'

'Always Simon Peter or John!' exclaimed Judas bitterly. Once more the boy cried out, and his father once more begged for help.

'It's an evil spirit that takes hold of him,' he said. 'Can you do nothing for him? Can you, after all, do nothing?' In desperation he cried out, 'Evil spirit! In the name of Jesus leave my boy alone!'

Judas turned on him roughly, angry that he had used the name of Jesus. 'Be quiet,' he commanded. Then to Andrew he said, 'Let me try.'

He took Andrew's place and held the boy firmly, commanding the evil spirit to leave the boy; but the boy began to throw himself about more wildly than ever. Judas bit his lip in humiliation. But just at that moment Andrew, pointing along the road, called out that the master was in sight, and one of the men rushed off to bring him to them.

In a very short time Jesus was with them, and the boy's father greeted him eagerly. He knelt before him, and the words tumbled from his lips as he begged for help.

'Master,' he cried, 'I beg you to look at my son, my only child.

He's an epileptic, and when the fit takes him he cries out and throws himself to the ground, hurting himself. I brought him to your disciples, but they could not cure him.'

Jesus looked at the disciples, 'So, my friends, you still lack faith,' he said. 'How much longer must I be with you? How much longer bear with you?' Then he looked with pity at the boy on the ground. 'How long has this been happening?' he asked the father.

'Ever since he was a small child, master,' the man replied. 'We believe it is an evil spirit; sometimes when it takes hold of him it drives him into the fire or into the water, as though it would destroy him. But if you can do anything have pity on us and help us.'

'*If* I can? Everything is possible for one who has faith.'

'I *have* faith,' said the father urgently, and as Jesus looked at him searchingly he added humbly, 'Help me where it fails.'

Jesus looked down at the boy and took a step nearer him, then said in a commanding voice, 'I command you to come out of him and never enter him again.'

At once the boy gave a loud cry and a shudder, and then lay perfectly still. The people around were silent for a moment, waiting, and then a voice cried, 'He's dead, the boy's dead.'

The father looked anxiously at Jesus while others in the crowd called out that the boy was dead and all hope gone. Jesus knelt by the boy and took his hand, saying softly, 'Stand up now, son.'

The boy opened his eyes and looked wonderingly at Jesus; then still holding his hand, he sat up and looked around him. 'I'm thirsty,' he said. Jesus helped him to his feet, while the crowd murmured in astonishment, then led him a little apart and sat down with the boy standing beside him. The father, nearly in tears, followed, and the disciples stood around them.

'My boy, my son,' cried the father. 'Thanks be to God my prayers are answered. Oh, master, I knew that you had only to speak and my boy would be cured.' He embraced the boy with tenderness, then he hurried into the house nearby to fetch water, while the boy stayed with Jesus.

Thomas was confused by what had happened. 'Master,' he said quietly, 'how was it that we were not able to drive the evil spirit away?'

'Because of your lack of faith,' replied Jesus. 'Indeed I tell you that if you only have faith like a grain of mustard seed you will say to that mountain "Move" and it will move. Have faith and you will find nothing impossible.'

'All of us?' asked Judas. 'Will we *all* be given the power to do such mighty works?' As he spoke he looked jealously at Peter, John and James, then went on, 'Or only the greatest among us? Andrew tried to cast out this devil and I tried and although we had faith, we failed. Who then, after you, shall be the greatest?'

'Whoever wishes to become great among you,' replied Jesus, 'must be the servant of all.'

'But in God's Kingdom,' went on Judas determinedly, 'who will be the great ones there?'

'Hear the truth,' said Jesus patiently. 'Unless your hearts are changed and you become like little children,' and as he spoke he looked down on the boy, and on other children who had gathered around him, 'you will not enter the Kingdom of Heaven at all. It is the man who makes himself humble as this little child, who is the greatest in the Kingdom of Heaven. Whoever in my name welcomes one such little child, welcomes me; and whoever welcomes me, welcomes Him that sent me.'

'Master,' said John, 'they say this boy's father was using your name to drive out the evil spirit, and they forbade him, since he was not one of us.'

Jesus waited before he replied, for the boy's father had returned from his house bringing a leather bottle of water and some cups. He handed them to Jesus and the disciples, and gave one to the boy, who drank thirstily. Jesus too drank, and then said, 'Do not forbid him, for no one who does a mighty work in my name can be quick to slander me. He who is not against us is for us. Indeed, whoever gives you a cup of water to drink because you are mine, that man shall not lose his reward.' A little girl climbed on to his knee and leant her head against his shoulder. 'But whoever causes one of these little ones who believe in me to sin, it would be better for him if a great millstone were hung about his neck and he were thrown into the sea. See that you do not despise any of these little ones, for I tell you that in Heaven their angels look upon the face of my Father for ever.'

PART 6

The Road to Jerusalem

As THE time drew near for Jesus to go back to his Father he resolutely set his face to go to Jerusalem. And although his disciples did not know all that lay ahead, yet they realized that many burdens were on his mind, and were anxious and disturbed.

The road to Jerusalem took them through Samaria and as they tramped along they talked together.

'The master seems to be troubled, John,' said James, voicing what was in all their minds. 'I don't like him to be alone,' and he moved as if to go to Jesus, but John stopped him, saying, 'Leave him, James. I think he walked ahead of us purposely. Everything seems to be changing, doesn't it? As though we were moving towards something.' He shuddered a little as he spoke.

'I wish we hadn't left Galilee,' said James. John was shocked.

'You mean,' he queried, 'not follow the master?'

But James said he didn't mean that—of course they would follow him wherever he went. But if only they could have stayed in Galilee—the air was free and friendly there. Besides, that was where they all belonged—except Judas.

'The air wasn't as friendly as you make out,' Judas reminded him. 'It wasn't safe for him to stay. Have you forgotten the warning brought by the Pharisees that Herod wanted to kill Jesus?'

'We're not likely to forget that,' said Peter with a smile, 'nor his reply: "Go and say to that fox that I shall continue my work so long as it is mine to do."'

'Yes,' went on John, 'and then he told us that he was bound to travel on towards Jerusalem because. . . .' his voice faltered a little, 'because it would not be right for a prophet to be killed anywhere but there. What did he mean by that?'

He looked at his brother James for guidance, and James put his arm round his shoulders, saying, 'I don't know, John. The only thing I know is that whatever danger there is for the master, even if it is death, we share it with him.' And the others murmured their agreement. All but Judas who was still perplexed and argumentative. 'But why should it be death?' he demanded. 'Why is he determined to die? For nearly three years we've been with him, and all the while I've dreamed of the time when the whole of Israel would be united as God's Holy Nation, and we'd march into Jerusalem with Jesus as our King. It could have happened. It so nearly came true. But look at us now: twelve dusty travellers along the road to Jerusalem—driven from Galilee, with empty purses, hated by the Pharisees, and no words of hope from Jesus. Nothing but this dreadful foreboding of death. What's become of the power and the glory of the Kingdom?'

'Wherever the master is, there is the Kingdom, Judas,' said Peter with conviction. 'And as for empty purses, we willingly left all to follow him, and when have we ever wanted for food and shelter?'

Before Judas could reply, Andrew interrupted them.

'Look,' he said, pointing, 'here come Philip and Nathaniel. They'll have found lodgings for us.'

They caught up with Jesus, as the two disciples, tired and dusty, joined him. Jesus asked them for news, but Philip replied, dejectedly, 'It's no use, master. That village you sent us to will have nothing to do with us. They say they will offer no shelter to Jews going to Jerusalem.'

John could scarcely contain his fury at this. 'Did they know,' he burst out, 'you came in the master's name?'

'Yes, of course,' said Nathaniel, 'and what's more they know that the master healed a Samaritan leper from their village only yesterday.'

'Blind ingratitude!' exploded James. 'They ought to be punished.'

By now John was beside himself with fury, and he turned to Jesus. 'Master,' he demanded, 'shall we call down fire from Heaven on this village to destroy it?'

But Jesus shook his head. 'James and John,' he said, 'you Sons of Thunder, are your thoughts only of vengeance? I did not come to destroy men's lives but to save them.'

'But they deserve it,' muttered James aggressively.

'We will go to another village,' said Jesus firmly, but Judas protested that they would find no welcome anywhere in Samaria.

'Then we will go on towards Jerusalem,' Jesus told them, and added, as he heard their weary murmurs, 'if you are weary and filled with vengeance now, how will you be when worse things befall us as indeed they must? Truly I say to you, the man who does not shoulder his cross and follow in my steps can be no disciple of mine.'

'His cross?' questioned Judas.

'Yes,' was the reply. 'We are going to Jerusalem, and the Son of Man will be handed over to the chief priests and rulers. They will condemn him to death and give him up to the Gentiles to be mocked and scourged and to be crucified.' He paused at the gasp from the nearest disciples, but went on before Judas had time to protest, and said softly, 'But after three days he will live again.'

Judas could contain himself no longer, and in anguish he asked, 'Master—*why* must it be so?'

'Truly, I tell you,' Jesus answered him, 'if the wheat grain does not fall into the soil and die it stays as it was, a single grain; but if it dies it yields abundantly.'

There was murmuring among the disciples. Thomas turned to Peter and Andrew, saying eagerly, 'We will go too, that we may die with him.' And Peter pushed forward to face Jesus, saying, 'Master, you know that we will follow you wherever you may go.'

But Jesus only smiled rather wearily, and said, 'Ah, Peter, the foxes have holes and the birds of the air have nests, but the Son of Man has nowhere to rest his head.'

So they walked on, resting awhile in the heat of the day, but making their way steadily in the direction of Jerusalem. Matthew and Simon the Zealot had gone ahead of them into the city of Jericho. They made their way along the crowded street, among the women carrying pots on their heads or with babies in their shawls, the merchants and lawyers, the tradesmen and beggars. They stopped under the shelter of a high wall.

'What a crowd!' said Matthew. 'I suppose we must expect it with the Passover so near. The closer we get to Jerusalem, the greater the crowds will be—and all, like us, looking for a night's lodging.'

'Let's hope they'll be friendly crowds,' said Simon.

Matthew was as cheerful as ever. 'Well, we won't know till we try,' he said. 'This looks a big house. I wonder who lives here—there seems to be plenty of room.' He looked up hopefully at the big house outside which they were standing, and then he noticed a blind man coming towards them, and spoke to the man who was leading him.

'Peace be unto you, friend,' said Matthew politely. 'We are looking for lodgings for the night.'

'You and everyone else,' said the man, laughing. 'How many? Just the two of you?'

'No,' replied Matthew. 'There'll be thirteen of us when our friends arrive.'

The man laughed again and shook his head, saying they would never get in anywhere all together. Matthew asked him who lived in the big house before which they were standing, and at once the blind man was roused to fierce speech.

'Don't have anything to do with *that* house,' he said. 'That's where Zacchaeus the tax collector lives—lives on the fat of the land, on money squeezed from the poor. A traitor, a thief, a friend of Rome.' He spat contemptuously, then turned to his friend. 'Isn't that so?' he asked, and the other laughed.

'That's so, Bartimaeus, 'he said, and added, 'Even though he's blind my friend knows when he's near an evil house.'

'Zacchaeus the tax collector, eh?' said Matthew, with a wry smile. 'The master's been entertained by a tax collector before now.'

'Who is your master?' asked the man, and when Matthew answered proudly that it was Jesus of Nazareth, Bartimaeus asked eagerly, 'Jesus the great prophet that they call the Son of David? The one who heals the sick and raises the dead?'

'That's right,' said Matthew, and Bartimaeus went on excitedly,

'They say he gives new eyes to the blind. Is it true, friend, is it true?'

'It is true,' agreed Matthew.

Bartimaeus could hardly believe it. 'Jesus, Son of David,' he kept murmuring to himself, as if the very sound of the name gave him hope.

His friend assured Matthew and Simon that if it was for Jesus they wanted lodgings they would have no difficulty, but that they would offend the people if they stayed in the house of the tax collector. And then he called out to some of the crowd, 'Hey, friends, have you heard the news? Jesus of Nazareth is on his way to Jericho.'

Some of the passers-by stopped and a woman carrying a baby exclaimed in wonder, 'Jesus of Nazareth coming to-day!' and others echoed her. A man asked if he was on his way to Jerusalem for the Passover, and another commented, 'There's courage for you. They say that many in Jerusalem would like to kill him.'

'They'll never kill Jesus; he has the secret of eternal life.'

Everyone turned to see who it was who spoke with such conviction. It was a richly dressed young man who stood among the crowd with his two servants. When they all looked at him he was suddenly embarrassed, but he stepped forward to speak to Matthew and Simon, asking them if they were disciples of the rabbi, Jesus. Matthew told him that they had been disciples for three years.

'Which way is he coming?' asked the young man, and was told it was from the north—through Samaria. The young man thanked him, then motioned to his servants to follow and went off down the road.

The crowd surged round Matthew and Simon, all talking at once, each asking that they should bring Jesus to them, either to stay with them, or to bless or heal their children.

'Tell him we're God-fearing folk in Jericho,' said one, and another assured them, 'He'll be safe here."

'When is he coming?' asked one of the women. 'We'll go and meet him,' and others clamoured again to have Jesus as their guest. In the hubbub nobody noticed the small figure of Zacchaeus, the tax collector, come out of his house. He joined the crowd and stood beside Matthew. Suddenly the people saw him—and at once there was a strange lull in their clamour. Matthew and Simon had not seen

As they tramped along they talked together

Matthew and Simon Zealot talking to Zacchaeus

The rich young man

Zacchaeus coming and were surprised by the sudden change in the crowd.

The silence was broken by one of the women. 'Traitor!' she hissed, and turned away, while the crowd muttered abuse.

'Friend of Rome!' said one of the men, and spat on the ground, before he too turned away, while the rest of the crowd moved off as if they could not bear the presence of the tax collector. Only the friend of Bartimaeus stood his ground and he taunted Zacchaeus with, 'Wait till Jesus comes, Zacchaeus. Then you'll see who's got the power, God's prophet or your Roman masters.'

He led Bartimaeus away, the blind man waving his stick angrily.

Matthew turned and looked at Zacchaeus, 'Peace be unto you, friend,' he said and Zacchaeus, touchingly grateful for the friendly greeting, replied, 'Unto you also let there be peace. You are strangers in Jericho?'

'We are,' said Matthew.

'Popular strangers, it seems,' said Zacchaeus. 'I'm afraid your friends went away because of me.' He smiled ruefully as he added, 'I'm not a popular man in Jericho.'

'Nor was I in my home town, and for the same reason, I think,' said Matthew, smiling. 'You are Zacchaeus, sir?'

'Yes,' he replied. 'I am the Chief of Customs. Nobody likes a tax collector.'

'I know one who does—our master,' said Matthew.

Zacchaeus asked who that master was, and when he was told it was Jesus of Nazareth, he immediately recognized the name.

'Jesus,' he queried incredulously, 'a friend of tax collectors?'

Matthew was delighted to reassure him. 'Nobody's too great a sinner to be his friend, I reckon. Look at me. You know, sir, how it is in the customs line—plenty of pickings on the side, and easy enough to cheat the accounts and squeeze more than is due from the people. I'm not saying it's that way with you, sir, but it was with me. Then Jesus came by one day and called me to follow him.'

'Just called you, and you went?' questioned Zacchaeus.

'Couldn't help myself,' maintained Matthew. 'He just looked at me, smiling and friendly and as though he *wanted* me.'

'It's a long time since anyone looked at me like that,' said Zacchaeus.

'That's what I felt,' said Matthew. 'He came back to my house with me. The "righteous" folk didn't like that, but he came all the same, and I gave a big feast—him and his friends and me and mine.'

Zacchaeus said he wished he could see him, and Matthew told him that he might, that he would be coming to Jericho that day, and that he and Simon had come on ahead to find lodgings.

'Do you think,' said Zacchaeus, clutching Matthew's arm as a sudden wild idea formed in his mind, 'do you think he would stay with me? I have a large house—I would welcome him.' Simon gave Matthew a warning nudge and Matthew, feeling that perhaps he had talked too much, answered cautiously. The whole town wanted to put Jesus up, he said; he seemed to be very popular here, not like in some of the places they'd been to. Simon joined in, to say bluntly that they did not want to lose that popularity.

Zacchaeus' hopes died. He knew only too well what they meant. 'I understand,' he said.

Simon was apologetic. 'No offence, sir,' he said, 'but you understand we don't know how he'll be received in Jerusalem. He has enemies there who will pick on anything to turn the people against him. We must protect him and not lose him the friends he has. Not now. It was very different in the beginning.'

'But we'll tell him you offered, sir, along with the others,' added Matthew.

'Come, Matthew,' said Simon, 'they're beginning to crowd to the gates to welcome him. We must get through if we want to meet him.'

They bade Zacchaeus farewell and hurried away. The little tax collector turned sadly into his rich house.

Meanwhile, on the road leading into Jericho, but a little distance from the town, the rich young man waited with his two servants in the shade of the palm trees, scanning the road, along which travelled many people, some on foot, some astride their laden donkeys, most of them making the pilgrimage to Jerusalem for the Passover. Presently he saw what he had hoped to see: in the distance Jesus and his disciples approaching. Motioning to his servants to wait, the young man ran along the dusty road to meet them. Jesus and the disciples stopped when they saw the man running towards them. Peter suggested it might be Matthew coming to warn them not to enter Jericho.

'It's not Matthew, nor Simon,' said James sagely. 'Too well dressed!'

'I know this man,' exclaimed Judas. 'He's one of the rulers of the synagogue. His family is one of the richest in Jericho.'

When the young man ran up, Jesus stepped forward to greet him, and as the young man knelt in the dusty road, he asked, 'What is it, my son?'

'Good master,' said the young man, 'tell me what I must do to inherit eternal life?'

'Why do you call me good?' asked Jesus. 'Only God is good. If you would have eternal life, keep His commandments.'

It was clear that the young man was rather disappointed and puzzled by this reply, and he asked at once which commandments.

'Do not murder,' said Jesus. 'Do not commit adultery; do not steal; do not bear false witness; honour thy father and thy mother.'

The young man rose, looked at Jesus, and answered with great sincerity, 'Master, I have kept all these since my boyhood, yet I know there is something more that I should do.'

Jesus looked at his earnest face, then took him by the shoulders and kissed him on the brow. 'My son,' he said, 'there *is* one thing more for you to do.'

'Yes?' asked the young man eagerly.

Jesus went on looking into his eyes with great love and hope. 'Sell everything you have,' he said, 'and give the money to the poor.' He saw the young man's eyes waver, and went on firmly, 'You will have treasure in Heaven. Then come and follow me.'

The boy's eagerness slowly faded. His face showed the struggle in his soul as he looked at the shabby, dusty little bunch of followers. His eyes went back to Jesus. He knew he could not make the sacrifice, and was ashamed. He hung his head, and slowly turned away. Jesus shared his sorrow as he stood looking after him, and the disciples gathered closer round him.

'How hard it is,' said Jesus, 'for men of wealth to enter the Kingdom of God.'

'Hard?' exclaimed Peter, astonished. 'Why, master?' and John questioned whether then it was only the poor who would enter.

'This was a good man, master,' said Judas. 'Why should it be made harder for him than for others, because he is rich?'

'It is very hard,' answered Jesus, 'for those who put their trust in riches to enter the Kingdom. This young man loves God, keeps the commandments and in all humility seeks the truth. But he has grown to depend upon his earthly riches, and so they have become a burden he cannot carry into the Kingdom.'

Judas asked rather cynically if the door to the Kingdom was so narrow, to which Jesus replied with a smile, that it was easier for a camel to go through the eye of a needle than for a rich man to enter into the Kingdom of God—a statement which made James and John burst into laughter.

But Judas wanted to pin Jesus down. 'You mean,' he asked, 'that for some salvation is impossible?'

'With God all things are possible,' was the reply.

'But, Lord,' protested Peter, '*we* gave up everything to follow you.'

'You did, Simon,' said Jesus, 'and I promise you that everyone who has given up his home and family to follow me will find himself re-paid a hundred times over in the work he will do here on earth, though not without persecution, and in the world to come he will have eternal life. Therefore, I say to you, make for yourselves purses that do not wear out. A treasure house in Heaven where no thief can come, and no moth destroy. For where your treasure is, there will your heart be also.'

'Master,' said James, 'we will gladly suffer persecution and we ask for no earthly riches, but grant that John and I may sit one on your right hand and one on your left when you come into the glory of your Kingdom.'

'You do not know what you are asking,' replied Jesus. 'Are you able to drink of the cup I have to drink, and suffer what I must?'

'Yes, master,' John assured him. 'We are able.'

'You will indeed share my suffering, James and John,' said Jesus. 'But as for the seats on my right hand or my left, they are not mine to bestow, but will be given to those for whom they have been prepared.'

Meanwhile, in the street leading into Jericho, a crowd was wait-ing for Jesus. For a better view, boys had swarmed up into the branches of the trees. Women were putting their children in front of the crowd so that they could see. And even the men stood and waited, talking together in excitement. Among them was Zacchaeus, but he was so short that there was no hope of his seeing anything on the road unless he could get through the crush of people. In front of him he saw Bartimaeus and his friend making their way through the crowd, and he followed them.

'Let us through—let my friend through, he's blind,' called the friend.

'It's no good,' said Bartimaeus. 'We'll never get near him for the crowds. I didn't know it would be like this.'

But a kindly man heard him and made way for him, saying he'd tell him when Jesus was coming. The two of them went through the gap in the crowd, and quickly Zacchaeus tried to slip through with them, but the man stopped him.

'Oh, no, you don't,' he said. 'There's nothing wrong with you. Get back to your own place.'

'I only thought,' said Zacchaeus, 'as I am so short I could perhaps stand in front. You are tall and could see over my head.'

But the man had recognized him, and said angrily that he wasn't going to give up his place for one of *his* kind, and he shoved Zacchaeus roughly back.

'Get back, Zacchaeus,' cried another man. 'Here's one time when your money won't help you. It's inches you want, not riches!'

There was laughter from the crowd at this sally, and Zacchaeus was pushed back amid more shouts, advising him to keep out of sight, because it was God-fearing folk that Jesus would want to see. Zacchaeus, sensitive to the jibes but still determined to see Jesus, looked up into the branches of a tree where two boys were already perched. When they saw him they began to laugh and pelted him with bits of bark and twigs. But to their astonishment he began to climb.

'Look at old Zacchaeus,' cried one of the boys; 'he's going to climb the tree!'

'No good coming up here, Zacchaeus,' called the other, 'we've no money to give you!' and they laughed at him, saying he would fall on his head, and hoping that he would. When Zacchaeus, panting a little, asked them to give him a hand up, they asked him what he wanted up there in the tree, anyway. He told them he had climbed up to see Jesus, and at that one of them reluctantly stretched out a hand to him, and he hauled himself up. Breathless but triumphant, he thanked them and settled himself on a branch, while the two boys grinned at each other.

Near the gates of the town another group of people were waiting, mostly women and excited children. Two little girls ran off to meet Jesus as they saw him coming along the road, and other children darted away from their mothers and flocked round him. Jesus stooped to pick up a baby as he talked to the little ones, and the watching women smiled to see how gently he spoke to them, and how happy the children were with him. Soon, the mothers too moved nearer to him, holding out their babies for a blessing, and crowding round to hear what he had to say. But Nathaniel and Philip intervened. 'Sorry,' said Philip, 'but you'll have to keep back. The rabbi has had a long journey. He can't be bothered with a lot of children now.' And Nathaniel backed him up, saying there were too many children round Jesus already, and they'd never get to town at this rate.

But meanwhile more children had appeared, laughing and shouting, and trying to attract his attention, so that a passing Pharisee asked irritably if no one could keep them quiet. 'There's no sense in all this uproar,' he said severely.

Jesus kissed the small baby in his arms and handed him back to his mother, who took him with pride and joy. Then he turned towards Philip and Nathaniel, who were trying to hold back a small boy who was shouting, 'I want to see Jesus. I want to see Jesus,' and he said, 'Let the little children come to me. Do not forbid them —for to such belongs the Kingdom of God.'

Philip and Nathaniel let the little boy through the crowd, and he ran to Jesus and took his hand. Jesus walked on, with the boy at his side, stopping now and then to bless the babies in their mothers' arms, and going slowly so that the children clinging to his robe could keep up with him. The crowd watching began to cheer and to call out.

'Hosanna!' they cried. 'Hosanna! Jesus, Redeemer of Israel!' 'Blessed be Jesus, prophet of God.' 'Hosanna!'

But suddenly above the acclamation and the cheering came a new cry—the voice of Bartimaeus, the blind man, calling, 'Jesus, Son of David, have pity on me!'

The Pharisee in front of him turned on him angrily, bidding him be silent, but his friend spoke up, saying, 'Mind what you're saying. Can't you see he's blind?'

Again Bartimaeus cried, more loudly this time, 'Son of David, have pity on me,' but Jesus had heard him the first time, and now bade John and Peter to bring the blind man to him. Peter went to him and told him to come, as Jesus was calling him; and Bartimaeus with a look of joy began to struggle out of his ragged coat.

'Here, take my coat,' he said to his friend; 'he mustn't see me in these old rags.' He held out his hands for guidance, and Peter and John led him to Jesus.

'My son,' said Jesus, 'what do you want me to do for you?'

'Master,' entreated Bartimaeus, 'let me see again.'

While the crowd watched, Jesus placed his hands over the man's eyes and said, 'Receive your sight.' Then he took his hands away. Bartimaeus blinked once or twice. Then his face lit up with incredulous joy as he looked first at his hands, holding them very near to his eyes, then, still blinking in the dazzling light, into the face of Jesus.

'I can see,' he said, his voice trembling. 'I can see. Praise be to God my sight has come back.' He began to shout in his excitement. 'I can see! Jesus, Son of David, has given me my sight.'

Jesus smiled at him. 'It is your faith that has done that,' he said. 'Go your way now, my son, and God's blessing be on you.'

He walked on into Jericho, with Bartimaeus following close behind him, still calling out above the cheering, 'I can see! Thanks to God. Thanks to Jesus, Son of David, I can see! I can see!'

More and more children ran to join Jesus, and soon he came to the tree through the branches of which Zacchaeus was peering, hoping for a sight of him. He did not cheer, but in his face was a great longing.

Under the tree Jesus stopped and looked up. The children looked up too, and some of them began to point and giggle. A look of apprehension came over Zacchaeus' sensitive face, but a second later he could scarcely believe his ears, for he heard Jesus calling up to him: 'Zacchaeus, make haste and come down for I am staying at your house to-day.'

The children's giggles stopped, and they turned and looked in astonishment at Jesus, while a murmur of disapproval ran through the crowd. The two boys in the tree stared open-mouthed as Zacchaeus began to scramble down.

Where there had been cheering, there was now a hushed, ominous silence. The disciples looked anxiously around at the watching, disapproving people.

'Master,' warned Simon Zealot, 'this Zacchaeus is the tax collector I told you of.'

'I know,' said Jesus.

'He's hated in Jericho, master,' added Judas. 'Are you wise to stay at his house? There's many good folk who would make you welcome.'

But Jesus would not be turned from his purpose. 'This man is lost in his loneliness, Judas,' he said. 'And the Son of Man came to seek the lost.'

'It's his own fault,' argued Judas, and Jesus replied, 'Perhaps, but if you had a hundred sheep and one of them had strayed, would you not leave the ninety-nine and go and look for the one that was lost?'

'You would indeed,' volunteered Philip, remembering his farming days. 'Many's the time I've done it.'

'And if you find it,' went on Jesus, 'does it not make you happier than the ninety-nine that did not wander away?'

Philip agreed heartily. 'That's true. Any shepherd would say the same.'

'The same is true of your Heavenly Father,' said Jesus. 'There is more joy in Heaven over one sinner that repents than over ninety-nine law-abiding people that have not gone astray.'

The crowd watched, silent and suddenly suspicious, as Zacchaeus came towards Jesus, hesitating but hopeful. Jesus turned and held out his hands to him, saying, 'Zacchaeus,' and the tax collector took his hands and called him, 'Jesus—master.'

Jesus told him to lead the way to his house, and with Peter, John, James and Andrew at his side he went with Zacchaeus through the silent, disappointed crowds.

A Pharisee expressed the feelings of them all. 'There's your "Son of David"—your "King of the Jews"! A man who even on the outskirts of the Holy City, and at this holy Passover time, will consort

'Let the little children come to me'

The healing of Bartimaeus

'If I have wronged any man I will pay him four times as much'

with our enemies, turn his back on the children of Abraham to be the guest of a traitor—an outcast. . . .'

Someone called 'Shame!' and the crowd grumbled among themselves, while Bartimaeus' friend said urgently to Simon, 'Can't you stop him? I told you he'd make enemies, and word quickly gets from here to Jerusalem.'

'I know,' answered Simon.

'He's lost everything now,' Judas said bitterly to Matthew, who pointed out that he had found Zacchaeus, and perhaps, ventured Bartimaeus boldly, Zacchaeus needed saving as much as he needed to be cured of his blindness.

But an angry man, overhearing them, said that Zacchaeus needed nothing—that he'd got all he wanted by making money out of the people.

In front of his house Zacchaeus spoke to Jesus.

'Lord, bear witness,' he said solemnly, 'to what I have to say. From this day forward I will give half of my fortune to the poor, and if I have wronged any man I will repay him four times as much.'

Jesus looked tenderly at Zacchaeus and at Bartimaeus, who had managed to reach his side. 'To-day,' he said, 'salvation has come to this house, for its master has returned to the family of God. It was for this that the Son of Man came: to seek and to save that which was lost.'

With that he turned and went into the house with Zacchaeus, followed by all the disciples, except Judas who remained at the gate, consumed with his own torment of doubt.

As the crowds dispersed grumblingly to their homes, the Pharisee watched Judas. Then he went over to him. 'Will you not follow your master?' he asked. Judas remained silent. 'Or are you beginning to distrust him?' When Judas still did not answer, he added, 'See how quickly the people turn against him. They'll do the same in Jerusalem if he goes there for the feast.'

But Judas could stand no more. He turned swiftly away and almost ran down the street. The Pharisee looked after him keenly, recognizing that here might be the weak place in Jesus' armour.

The busy streets of Jerusalem were thronged with people of all nationalities who had come there for the Passover.

In the courtyard of the house of Caiaphas, the High Priest, the temple police were on duty, for within the house the Sanhedrin was in consultation. In low voices Nicodemus and the Pharisee who had been in Jericho and seen Jesus there were talking together. Nicodemus asked if Jesus would come to the feast, and the Pharisee replied that he was sure of it, that he had heard that Jesus had already reached Bethany and . . . but here they were interrupted by Caiaphas, who in icy tones called 'Nicodemus!'

Nicodemus looked up with a start.

'If you and your friend have anything to discuss,' said Caiaphas, 'I feel sure it must be a matter for the Sanhedrin to hear. May we please have no private conversations.'

Nicodemus looked embarrassed and hastened to explain that they were talking of the man Jesus of Nazareth.

'A matter of very great importance,' interrupted Caiaphas, 'and one to which I was just about to refer. However,' he added with great sarcasm, 'perhaps you would tell us what *special* news you have.'

'I have no special news, my lord,' said Nicodemus. 'I have only seen the man Jesus once, and that many months ago. Our friend here has more information, having recently seen the Galilean party in Jericho.'

'Indeed?' said Caiaphas. 'And what impression did you receive?'

The Pharisee took a deep breath. Although he was scared of Caiaphas, he was eager to have his say and was going to make the most of this opportunity.

'My lord Caiaphas,' he said, 'since you invite me to speak, I would like to draw the attention of the Sanhedrin to the charges that have been made in Galilee and Judea against this man Jesus and his followers. I have here a list.'

But Caiaphas was impatient, and dismissed this with a wave of the hand. 'I think,' he said, 'the Sanhedrin is aware of the charges, my friend: eating with unwashed hands, casting out devils by the power of Satan, claiming to be in possession of special powers, blasphemy. We know all this. What new things have you to tell us?'

'My lord,' said the Pharisee pompously, 'did you know that he consorts with heathens and sinners?'

Once more Caiaphas dismissed this impatiently. 'Yes, yes,' he said, but the Pharisee was not to be checked and went on. 'That in spite of this the people call him the "Son of David"—"The King of the Jews"?' The Pharisee noted with satisfaction that Caiaphas was now taking notice, and he went on confidently, 'That even now men are saying he is the Messiah.'

But another Pharisee poured scorn on his words.

'What nonsense,' he said. 'How can the Messiah come from Galilee? Do not the scriptures say that the Messiah would come from David's town of Bethlehem?'

'You are uninformed,' said Caiaphas sharply. 'This Nazarene *was* born in Bethlehem.'

'Then, my lord,' asked Nicodemus, 'do you think . . . ?'

There was a tense silence before Caiaphas asked in an icy tone, 'Do I think *what*, Nicodemus?'

But Nicodemus saw the danger he was in, and faltered as he answered. 'I—I was going to suggest, my lord, that perhaps we are too hasty in our judgment of this man.' He paused at the murmur that rose from the other members of the council; then went on, still hesitantly, 'Is it not at least possible that he may be . . . ?'

'May be *what?*' asked Caiaphas, in the same tone.

But now Nicodemus was really intimidated, and could only answer lamely, 'A teacher, sent by God.'

'Take care, Nicodemus,' said Caiaphas sternly. 'Do not forget that this is a *priestly* council. We know that you Pharisees are zealous in your pursuit of righteousness, in your hopes for a restored Israel, in your faith in the promised Messiah. Take care lest your zeal lead you into danger. Do not forget that it is only by the work of the priests and Sadducees that our holy faith has survived in Israel, governed as it is by Rome.' He looked at the listening councillors and went on, 'We still have our temple in which to worship freely, our rulers, our priests, our court of justice. But let it be thought that we Jews support the claims of a man who sets himself up as "King of Israel" and you will see how quickly the Romans will upset our religion and our race itself.'

He paused, as a murmuring broke out among the Pharisees. 'I have spoken,' he said, 'as Chief Priest of the temple. Perhaps one of your learned colleagues will explain to you why Jesus cannot be, as you suggest, "a teacher sent from God." '

The Pharisee from Jericho spoke up without hesitation. 'This man Jesus does not come from God. He breaks the Sabbath.'

And another added, 'We are disciples of Moses. We know that God spoke to Moses, but as for this man, who knows what evil power may be in him?'

'How could an evil man do such miracles?' asked Nicodemus bravely, but the first Pharisee answered him with scorn. 'He is possessed by a devil—he is mad!'

'He does not talk like one possessed,' returned Nicodemus. 'Can a mad man open blind men's eyes?'

'Are you bewitched like the Galileans?' asked the Pharisee angrily, and another joined in with more reasoned argument. 'My friend,' he said, 'you do not seem to be clear in your mind as to the nature of the charges against Jesus. It is not the fact that he heals the sick that we hold against him, but that he claims to forgive men's sins. Not the fact that he is a popular religious leader, but that he teaches men to break the Sabbath—to leave their homes and families to follow him, to set at naught the teaching of their forefathers, and, most serious of all, he allows the common people to believe that he is the Messiah.'

'And,' added the first Pharisee obstinately, 'makes friends for himself among the enemies of Israel.'

'Well,' said Caiaphas smoothly, 'our views may differ as to the seriousness of *that* charge, but we are all united, I think, in our realization of the danger to our religion and our nation if this man is allowed to make a disturbance in Jerusalem during Passover week.'

'Agreed, agreed,' said the Pharisee.

'I think myself,' continued Caiaphas, 'that the people of Jerusalem will not be as easily taken in by fine words and miracles as the peasants in the north, but we must be on our guard.'

The Pharisee warned Caiaphas that he was mistaken if he thought Jesus' popularity was confined to the north, since even as that moment crowds from Jerusalem were flocking to Bethany, where Jesus and his disciples were expected to stay at the house of Lazarus.

'Ah yes,' said Caiaphas. 'Lazarus, the man who died and was restored to life.'

'Exactly,' said the Pharisee. 'You will remember the stir and excitement that incident caused. The excitement is greater than ever now that there is not only Lazarus to gape at but the man who raised him from the dead. If we just let him be, the whole populace will believe in him; and as you have said, the Romans will put an end to our worship and our nation. The danger is great. It is here and now, my lord.'

Nicodemus had risen to his feet in protest, and now his fear was forgotten and he spoke with a rush of words. 'My lord,' he said, 'I protest! Surely our laws do not condemn a man without giving him a hearing—without finding out what he is really doing?'

'Have you no sense?' replied Caiaphas. 'Do you not realize that it is to your advantage that one man should die for the people, rather than that the whole nation should perish?'

As the Pharisee had guessed, Jesus stayed that night in Bethany at the home of Lazarus. Next morning James and John rose early, and came into the courtyard of the house where they found Lazarus' sister, Martha, busily sweeping.

'You're up early, Martha,' said John, greeting her.

Martha enjoyed her housework, but she liked everyone to know that she was the practical one who made everything run smoothly in the home.

'Someone had to get up early to clean up after last night,' she said. 'People were even camping here in the courtyard, hoping to catch a glimpse of Jesus. They've only just gone,' she added.

'Wasn't it wonderful getting such a welcome so near to the gates of the city?' said John happily. 'It cheered us all, I can tell you.'

'Oh, we've had the same sort of thing for weeks now, ever since the news of Lazarus got around,' said Martha. 'People have been coming from quite distant parts to see the "man who died." But there's never been as many as last night. We've got the Passover pilgrims as well now, you see.' She paused in her sweeping to ask, 'Is the master coming out now?'

'He's out already,' said James. 'He was up before dawn and went to the Mount of Olives to pray.'

'There now,' said Martha, surprised that anyone should be up and out without her knowing, 'I must get his breakfast. He'll want to be off early to the city, I dare say, before the crowds start bothering him again.'

'He won't be entering the city quietly, but in triumph!' said James in some excitement. 'He's given us our orders. We're to go into Bethphage and bring the ass that's waiting for him there. He's going to ride into the city like a King.'

'Like a King!' marvelled Martha, rather awed.

'Remember what the scriptures say,' said John. ' "Fear not, O daughter of Zion, for behold thy King cometh to thee, meek and lowly and riding upon an ass." '

James urged John to hurry, and they took leave of Martha, and went off to fetch the ass. But Martha was very excited by the news. She went to the door of the house and called, 'Mary, Mary, where are you?'

When her sister answered, she called to her to bring the pitcher and go to the well for water, for there was much work to be done. Mary came out of the house. She was younger than Martha, and very beautiful. She explained that she was looking for the master.

'He's out already,' Martha told her briskly, busily getting on with a host of jobs. 'So are James and John. Such a day we've got before us—and all week too, I shouldn't wonder. If the master comes back here at nights as I hope he will, we'll give a big banquet for him before the festival. But to-day is the great day. Now off to the well with you. I must see to the breakfast.'

But Mary was suddenly and unaccountably afraid. 'What happens to-day?' she asked, her eyes wide with apprehension.

'Why,' said Martha, pleased with her knowledge, 'to-day Jesus will ride into Jerusalem like a King.'

'Riding to be a King,' echoed Mary. 'Or riding to die?' She shuddered as she spoke, for she alone sensed the foreboding behind the triumph. 'Oh, master,' she murmured. 'Oh, master.'

While John and James were away fetching the ass, Jesus knelt on the Mount of Olives, praying. Presently he rose and looked across at the city of Jerusalem, and he spoke softly, with no one to hear him.

'O Jerusalem, Jerusalem,' he said. 'You who slay the prophets and stone those who are sent to you. How often have I longed to gather your children to me, as a hen gathers her chickens under

The council of the Sanhedrin

'Blessed is he that comes in the name of the Lord'

her wings, and they would not come. Now you will not see me until you say, "Blessed be he that cometh in the name of the Lord."'

Then he turned and walked down to Bethany, back to the house of Lazarus, where the disciples awaited him with the ass on which he was to ride into the city.

Along the way leading to Jerusalem crowds were already gathered, waving and cheering and crying out, 'Blessed be he that comes in the name of the Lord. Hosanna! Hosanna to the son of David!'

A Syrian pilgrim newly arrived in Jerusalem wondered what it was all about, and managed to attract the attention of a wildly cheering man. 'What is it? Who is coming?' the pilgrim asked; and was told it was Jesus, the prophet from Galilee, whom men called the Messiah. And the cheering man went on shouting, and was echoed by the women and children on every side, calling 'Jesus! Jesus, son of David!' 'Hosanna to the King of Israel' and 'Blessed is he that comes in the name of the Lord.'

Soon the shouting and the cheering broke out with even greater enthusiasm, for now at last Jesus appeared, riding on the ass, with his disciples walking beside him.

Judas' eyes darted swiftly over the faces of the crowd, as if he were trying to sum up the value of all this tumultuous welcome.

A Pharisee broke from the crowd and hurried up to Jesus, saying urgently, 'Master, do you hear what the people are shouting? Rebuke them, bid them hold their peace.'

But Jesus replied, 'I tell you if these keep silent the very stones would cry out.'

And he rode on, through the cheering multitudes. In the fields on either side the labourers and the shepherds and the gleaners looked up from their work, and a man grinding corn dropped his work and ran to join the throng. Some boys tore branches from a tree and climbed on a wall to wave and shout; and men followed their example, tearing down branches to wave in the air and then throw down under the feet of the ass.

And still Jesus rode on, his face looking towards Jerusalem. And as he drew nearer to the city, he looked across at it deeply moved, and spoke softly, his words unheeded by the noisy crowd.

'Ah Jerusalem, if you too could understand the ways that can bring you peace. But your eyes are blind. Indeed a time is coming when your enemies will encircle you and press you hard on every side, and bring down in ruins both you and your children. And all because you did not recognize the time when the Lord visited you.'

The shouts of the crowd had become a rhythmic chant and from the city the singing could be heard coming nearer and nearer, 'Blessed be he that cometh in the name of the Lord.'

The streets of Jerusalem were thronged with foreign pilgrims, come for the Passover, as well as the usual crowds of a busy city: Pharisees, beggars, merchants, servants, women and children. As they heard the shouts and the singing around the city gate they questioned one another, asking who was coming and what it was all about. When they were told it was Jesus of Nazareth, the Galilean prophet, coming to the feast, they too began to take up the cry, and soon the streets of the city rang with their shouts of 'Hosanna!' 'Hosanna to the son of David,' 'Blessed is he that comes in the name of the Lord,' 'Blessed be the King.'

And through them all Jesus rode into Jerusalem.

PART 7

The Last Week

WHEN Jesus entered Jerusalem it was the time of the Passover and in the temple courtyard there were merchants and farmers selling animals and pigeons for sacrifice, and there were money changers, too, with their money spread out before them on stalls. From the noise and confusion it might have been a market place rather than the temple of God.

As Jesus and his disciples came in one of the priests who had been at the meeting of the Sanhedrin noticed him and pointed him out to his companion.

'There's the Nazarene,' he said. 'The tall man in the white robe.'

'He hasn't much of a following to-day,' said the other. 'They're all too busy buying and selling to pay attention to him. But if he begins to preach we'll have to watch him.'

'I wonder if he's really as dangerous as we think,' mused the second priest. 'I confess I'd like to hear him speak.'

'You'll probably get your chance to-day,' he was assured. 'Look, he's beginning to attract a crowd already.'

They moved across the court, passing a money changer's table, where two Syrian pilgrims stood waiting for their money. The money changer counted it out: 'Twenty, thirty, forty. Thank you, sir,' he said, handing it over. But one of the pilgrims protested that he had been given too little—that fifty and not forty pieces of silver was the right exchange for his gold.

The money changer was oily in his manner, but he would not give more. 'Forty—forty to-day, sir,' he assured the pilgrims. 'That's the official temple rate. Pay your temple tax over there. Sacrificial lambs in the courtyard beyond.'

On every side was the sound of barter, mixed with the lowing of cattle, the bleating of sheep, and the cooing of pigeons. Men with huge crates on their backs staggered in to unload more goods for sale, and there were porters obviously using the temple as a short cut through the city. The merchants were crying their wares: 'Pigeons, pigeons for the Passover, lovely fat pigeons'; the money changers were offering higher rates and outbidding their neighbours, while temple guards were urging customers to pay their tax.

Through this medley of people the two priests made their way towards the steps on which Jesus was standing with his disciples around him, and where a crowd of pilgrims was beginning to collect.

'Have you forgotten that this is the House of God?' they heard Jesus say. 'Would you dishonour His holy place with your buying and selling, your bargaining and cheating?'

A pigeon seller laughed scornfully at this. 'Oho, I wouldn't call this a holy place,' he said, grinning. 'It's the Court of the Gentiles.'

'The Court of the Gentiles,' said Jesus, 'is a room in my Father's house. Remember what Solomon said, "When the stranger, who is not of thy people Israel, but is come from a far country, shall come and pray in this house, then hear thou from the Heavens that all people of the earth may know that this house which I have built is called by thy name." '

'Who do you think you are?' asked the pigeon seller rudely. 'The high priest?' There was uneasy laughter from some of the listeners, and he went on, 'No, Caiaphas knows better. *He* knows that the temple needs money and we have our living to earn too.'

Ignoring Jesus, he turned with his cages and began to shout more loudly than ever: 'Pigeons! Lovely fat pigeons for the Passover. Only two pieces of silver. Pigeons for sacrifice. . . .'

Unwilling to hear more that might stir their consciences, the

people began to drift away from Jesus, arguing among themselves
about what he had said, but soon joining in the cries and hubbub
of the temple.

Jesus looked on the scene before him, then picked up a piece of
rope that had been used for tethering an animal. With determination he bore down upon a money changer, the startled people
scattering on all sides before him. The money changer jumped up
in bewilderment, and Jesus, with one stroke of his 'whip,' swept the
money off the table on to the floor. The money changer leapt to
save it, and in the confusion the table was overturned.

'Take these things from my Father's house,' commanded Jesus,
but the man protested bitterly at what he had done.

Jesus silenced him. 'Is it not written,' he asked, ' "My house shall
be called a house of prayer for all people"? But you have made it
a den of robbers.' With swift movements he walked between the
tables, scattering the merchants. More tables were overturned, and
money and goods flew in all directions.

Meanwhile the two priests had been watching all that had happened, and now they mounted the steps where Jesus had been, to
get a better view of the confusion below them. Judas saw them
coming, and slipped behind a pillar out of sight.

'Well,' he heard the first priest say, 'there's your Jesus of Nazareth,
the most dangerous man our nation has known.'

'He has courage,' maintained the second priest.

'A man without fear is doubly dangerous,' went on the first
priest. 'The rabble love a scene of violence. See how they are flocking to him now. This defiance is a challenge to all the temple
stands for—a challenge to our priestly authority.'

His companion was incredulous. 'You think he means to start a
revolution?' he asked.

'It may come to revolution if he is allowed to go on,' said the first
priest. 'Though he is too crafty to preach sedition, there's many
call him the Messiah or the King of Israel.'

Judas listened as they went on discussing the matter, saying that
Jesus was too clever to call himself the Messiah, and that the Pharisees had tried to catch him out on many occasions, but he was
skilled in argument and always managed to turn the question. They

thought that Caiaphas had been inclined to minimize the danger, but that after this sacrilegious exhibition he would be bound to take action.

'He'll order Jesus' arrest,' said the first priest confidently.

The second priest pointed out that they would have to choose their time carefully, and that to arrest him publicly might create the very disturbance they wanted to avoid.

'Yes,' agreed the other. 'What we need to do is to find him alone, to take him unawares. Go and mingle with the crowd, question him if you can, but be careful. I will go and report to Caiaphas.'

They went off in different directions, and from behind a pillar came Judas. He had heard all that had been said, and now he stood looking after them, deeply troubled.

In another part of the temple Jesus stood with an excited crowd around him. Among them were three Pharisees talking together, and one of these was Nicodemus, who was stoutly maintaining that no man on the side of Rome would dare to challenge the priests' authority as Jesus had done.

'I'll ask him, then,' said the first Pharisee. 'I'll ask him what he thinks of the Roman tax'; and he called out, 'Rabbi, rabbi!' and when Jesus asked him what he wanted to know, he said, craftily, 'You teach the way of God sincerely, and you're not afraid of anyone in authority. Tell us then, is it lawful to pay taxes to Caesar or not?'

The crowd felt that here was a question that touched them all, and they murmured in sympathy.

'Should we pay them, or should we not?' persisted the Pharisee.

But Jesus was too wise to be trapped. 'So you would put me to the test, eh? Hypocrite!' he said, and he asked for a coin that he might look at it.

The Pharisee took one from his purse and, pushing through the crowd, handed it to Jesus, who asked, 'Whose likeness is this? Whose inscription?'

The Pharisee replied that it was Caesar's. 'Then,' said Jesus, 'pay to Caesar the things that are Caesar's, and to God the things that are God's. It is your duty to God you should be thinking of, and your duty to Him is to love Him and keep His commandments.'

Jesus rebukes the money changers

'A man without fear is doubly dangerous'

'Pay to Caesar the things that are Caesar's'

The Pharisee looked foolish, but the crowd delighted at his discomfiture and murmured approval.

'Rabbi Jesus,' called Nicodemus, and Jesus, recognizing him, hailed him, 'Nicodemus!'

'Would you tell us, rabbi,' said Nicodemus, 'which commandment you consider to be the greatest of all?'

Jesus replied, 'The first is, "Thou shalt love the Lord thy God with all thy heart, with all thy soul, with all thy mind and with all thy strength." The second is this, "Thou shalt love thy neighbour as thyself." There is no other commandment greater than these.'

'You have said truly, rabbi,' said Nicodemus; 'to love God with the whole heart, with understanding and with strength, and to love one's neighbour as oneself is much more than burnt offerings and sacrifice.'

'My friend,' said Jesus, 'you are not far from the Kingdom of God.'

But now another voice was heard. It was the second priest who had said he would listen to Jesus in order to report to Caiaphas, and now he thought he saw his chance to catch Jesus out, and so have still more to report.

'Rabbi,' he asked, 'we have seen you take upon yourself to drive from the temple those who lawfully sell animals for the Passover sacrifice. May we know by what authority you do these things?'

'I will ask you a question,' replied Jesus; 'answer me and I will tell you by what authority I do these things. Was the mission of John the Baptist from Heaven or from men?'

But before the priest could answer a Pharisee stopped him. 'Careful,' he warned. 'If you say "From Heaven" he will ask, "Then why didn't we believe him?"' The crowd joined in the argument, saying that John was a true prophet, a prophet of God, and that John's authority came from Heaven, they were sure of that.

The priest was alarmed.

'But this rabble all believe he was sent by God,' he murmured to the Pharisee. 'They'll turn on us if we say "from men."'

Jesus interrupted them. 'Answer me,' and the priest had to confess that they didn't know.

'Neither will I tell you,' said Jesus, 'by what authority I do these things. For if you had known John you would know me. But I will tell you a story. A man planted a vineyard and dug a pit for the wine press, and let it out to some wine-dressers while he went into another country. When the grapes were ripe he sent a servant to the tenants to get from them his share of the fruit of the vineyard. But they took the servant and beat him, and sent him away empty-handed. Again he sent to them another servant, and they sent him away wounded like the other. And he sent another, and him they killed, and so with many others; some they beat and some they killed. He had still one other, a beloved son. Finally he sent him to them saying, "They will honour my son." But those tenants said to one another, "This is the heir. Let us kill him and the inheritance will be ours." And they took him and killed him and cast him out of the vineyard.'

He paused for a moment, and the people were silent. He went on, 'What do you think the owner of the vineyard will do?' Again there was no sound. 'I will tell you. He will come and destroy those tenants and give the vineyard to others.' At this the Pharisees began to protest, with a murmur of 'shame.' Jesus gave them time to answer him, but when they did not, he said in a louder voice, and looking straight at them and at the priests, 'Have you not read this in your scriptures? "The very stone that the builders rejected has become the chief stone of the corner: this was the Lord's doing and it was marvellous in our eyes"?'

Later that evening Jesus and his disciples returned to Bethany, and, tired after the long day, were glad to eat a meal which Martha put before them. She came into the courtyard where they sat, bearing dishes of fruit and put them on the low table round which they were sitting.

'What, *more* food, Martha?' asked Matthew.

Martha was pleased and assured them they would not go short of food while she was there to serve them. Thomas leaned forward to help himself to some dates, while he said comfortably how good it was to be among friends and away from the crowds for a little, for he didn't like city crowds.

Philip helped himself, too, to some fruit. 'But don't you find it exciting?' he asked. 'I love to see all those pilgrims crowding the streets and the temple; and everywhere we go hearing them talk of the master. Even people from pagan countries seem to know of him.'

'Is that so?' asked Martha, smiling proudly. Philip told her that on the day before two Greeks had come up and asked to be taken to Jesus. Nathaniel said that this visit to Jerusalem had been a glorious triumph, and that he would never forget their entry into the city.

Philip pointed through the gateway along the road. 'From here,' he said, 'you can see the very road we took, only then it was thronged with a cheering multitude, and the master riding in the middle of them.'

'It was a triumph in the temple all right,' added Matthew, coming up beside Martha. 'It was as though the master had come home to his Father's house and found thieves there—the way he drove them out! You should have seen them, Martha. I thought there'd be trouble with the priests, but they didn't dare lay a finger on him.'

Martha looked rather anxiously to where Jesus and the other disciples sat, and almost to herself, she said, 'They've been here, though.'

Matthew did not hear her, and he offered now to take the dish and serve the others, for she had eaten nothing herself. But Martha wouldn't hear of it. She liked to see for herself, she said, that everyone had what he wanted. She moved the dishes along the table to where Jesus sat, with Mary at his feet, and Lazarus beside him. She beckoned to her brother, who came to her, and Judas followed quietly and listened to what was said.

'Lazarus,' said Martha, 'you should tell the master of the men who questioned us.'

'What men?' asked Lazarus.

'The men the priests sent to ask where Jesus stayed at night time,' said Martha with some impatience.

But Lazarus saw no reason why he should tell Jesus. It was peaceful enough now, and nobody had been near.

'I think you should tell him all the same,' said Martha firmly. 'We want things to stay peaceful for him. After all he's done for us we don't want to be the cause of trouble following him here.'

'You think he may choose not to stay with us any more?' asked Lazarus in surprise.

'It might be safer,' said Martha shortly.

But Lazarus protested that they would never find lodgings anywhere else, and Martha agreed, but said there were caves between Bethany and Jerusalem. She pointed in the direction of the city, and added, 'There's the Garden of Gethsemane by the brook Kedron. That's a place that Jesus loves. It's quiet and has trees and caves for shelter, and no one but us knows that he goes there.'

Lazarus nodded and then moved with his sister towards where Jesus sat with his disciples. His other sister, Mary, sat at the master's feet and it seemed as though her love was mixed with anxiety.

John had been thinking, and his voice came now out of a peaceful silence. 'Master, in that story about the man whose servants and whose only son were killed by the tenants of his vineyard. . . .'

'Yes?' Jesus prompted him.

'If the owner of the vineyard is God, then the vineyard is His Kingdom, and the tenants the children of Israel.'

'That is so, John,' said Jesus.

'Well, you said that the owner would take away the vineyard and let it out to others.'

'Yes,' said Jesus.

'But the priests and the Pharisees profess to do the will of God,' persisted John. 'Why, then, should the Kingdom be taken from them?'

Judas moved nearer and listened with keen attention while Jesus answered.

'I will tell you a story of another vineyard,' said Jesus, 'and you shall answer your question yourself. A certain man had two sons. To the first he said, "My son, go and work in my vineyard to-day," and the son answered, "No, I will not." But later he was ashamed and changed his mind, and went and worked as his father had asked. Then the man went to his other son and asked him to go and work, and he answered, "I will, sir." But he did not go. Which son carried out his father's will?'

'The first,' said John.

'That is why I say,' said Jesus, 'that there are many sinners who are nearer to the Kingdom of God than some of the priests and Pharisees who keep the letter of the law but disregard its meaning.'

John looked with affection on him. 'Dear master,' he said, 'when you explain these things to us you are like a light shining on all the dark and difficult places.'

Jesus looked at him with love, and then round at the others. He spoke sadly, and with a certain urgency.

'My children,' he said, 'for a little while the light is in your midst. Walk while you still have the light, lest the darkness overtake you. For the man who walks in the dark does not know which way he is going. Put your trust in the light while you have it, and so become children of light.'

Because he needed reassurance, Peter spoke lightly. 'Master,' he said, 'you speak sadly. All is well now. We twelve are together and among friends. You have won over the people of Jerusalem.' He hesitated and his next words were almost a question. 'The danger we feared is passed.' It was as though he were entreating Jesus to say that what he had told them about being handed over to the Gentiles to be killed was not true after all. But Jesus said. 'Children, you and I have but a short time together.'

There was a gasp and Mary put her hand on Jesus' knee crying, 'Master!'

But Jesus went on, speaking quietly and firmly as though to children, 'After a little while you will see me no longer; and again in a little while you will see me; because I am going back to the Father.'

Only Mary moved. She rose and went swiftly into the house. The disciples waited, puzzled and afraid, while Judas stared hard at Jesus. The excitement of the last few days had in many ways revived his hopes of a 'kingly' Messiah, but his fear and distrust had returned in the temple when he learned from the priests how united were the religious leaders against Jesus. And now Jesus talked about 'going back to the Father.' To Judas it was an admission of failure. Either it meant that he was determined to play the part of a martyr or that he was going to leave them, to escape and let them take the consequences. With a shock Judas realized he didn't trust Jesus any more. He was at this moment very nearly mad. The other disciples began protesting among themselves, asking one another what Jesus had meant, and saying that surely he would not leave them; and yet he had said in 'a little while,' how long would that be?

' "Going back to the Father," ' said Nathaniel slowly. "I don't understand. Do you, Judas?'

'No,' said Judas. 'I don't understand.'

Jesus let them talk among themselves for a little and then he said, 'Do you still not understand? Did I not tell you while we were on the road what would happen to the Son of Man in Jerusalem?'

He was interrupted by Mary, who had returned from the house with a flask of precious ointment. The disciples drew aside to let her pass, and watched her as she went straight to Jesus and knelt at his feet, looking at him with great love and sadness. Then she broke the top off the jar, poured some of the precious ointment over his feet, and then anointed his forehead with it.

This was the last straw for Judas. He knew the value of the ointment, and was disgusted by what she had done. All his pent up anger and bewilderment exploded, with 'What a stupid and sinful waste. Why, this ointment could have been sold for three hundred pieces of silver, and the money given to the poor.'

Jesus checked him sternly. 'Do not rebuke her, Judas,' he said. 'She has done something for me which is beautiful and kind. You have the poor among you always. You can do good to them when you wish. But me you have not always. She has done what she could. She has anointed my body beforehand to prepare it for burial. And I tell you that wherever in the world the gospel is preached, what this woman has done will also be told, so that she shall not be forgotten.'

Without a word Judas turned on his heel and left the place. He stumbled blindly along the road, and soon he found himself on the outskirts of Jerusalem. With slow, irresolute steps he began to walk towards the house of Caiaphas.

Caiaphas was holding a meeting of the council of the Sanhedrin. In front of him stood a young soldier, Captain Malchus, the captain of the temple guard. The high priest was upbraiding him because he had failed to bring in Jesus as he had been ordered to do. He and his soldiers could not, said the captain, lay hands on him; and to Caiaphas' curt query whether he meant could not or would no, he answered falteringly, 'Well, there'd have been a fine disturbance if we'd used force, my lord, but. . . .'

'But that wasn't the reason?' Caiaphas pressed him.

'No, my lord,' said Malchus, gaining courage. 'It was the way

'Wherever in the world the gospel is preached, what this woman has done will also be told, so that she shall not be forgotten'

The Last Supper

he talked. I'd never heard him before nor ever heard anyone like him.'

Caiaphas was coldly contemptuous. 'You mean you let yourself be taken in like the common rabble? You should learn from your betters, captain. Does a single ruler of the synagogues or any of the Pharisees believe in this man? No. It is the ignorant rabble who know nothing of the law who are bewitched. You should look to your duty as an officer, captain, or you may find you hold that rank no longer.'

With a curt nod, Caiaphas dismissed him, and turned to Annas, his father-in-law, an old, cautious man who had been the high priest some years before. Annas said he thought Caiaphas had been running a great risk in sending guards to arrest Jesus publicly, since the whole world appeared to be running after him; Caiaphas replied that they felt the matter was urgent. A great disturbance had been caused on the day when Jesus had taken upon himself to drive the money changers from the temple, and it had seemed necessary to assert their authority at once.

'And what charge,' asked Annas, 'would you have brought against him if your captain had fetched him here?'

'The charges are numerous, my lord,' replied Caiaphas shortly, 'but the outstanding one is that of blasphemy.'

'For which the sentence is death. I see,' the old man mused. 'I suppose you have witnesses?'

'Witnesses could certainly be found,' said Caiaphas. 'There is no doubt that once arrested and charged, the council will find him guilty.'

The members of the council murmured their assent, and Caiaphas went on, 'We shall be grateful for the benefit of your wisdom and experience, my lord, if there is any advice you have to offer us.'

'Your duty is clear,' said Annas. 'You must arrest this man. Put him on trial on a charge of blasphemy and if the evidence is sufficient, sentence him to death. But,' he added, 'you will have to find a way to arrest him secretly. Moreover, since only the Roman Governor has power to authorize an execution, you will need to think up some other charge than blasphemy to satisfy the Romans. Blasphemy would mean little to them, I fear.'

Caiaphas replied that he was confident that the Romans, too, would recognize the threat to their power, but he realized that the difficulty would be to take Jesus quietly, without the people knowing that it was being done.

Meanwhile in the courtyard outside, Malchus paced up and down on guard duty, still smarting a little from the scorn of Caiaphas' words. Suddenly a figure moved in the shadows, keeping out of sight, and at once Malchus challenged him. There was no reply. He strode across the courtyard and asked him roughly, 'What are you doing here?'

'I wish to speak to the lord Caiaphas.'

Malchus seized a torch and held it so that the light fell on the man's face.

'I know your face,' he said. 'Aren't you one of the Galileans that follow Jesus of Nazareth?'

'I'm not a Galilean, but I did follow Jesus.'

'I see,' said Malchus, trying to sum up the situation. 'And what do you want with the high priest?'

'My business is private.'

Malchus hesitated for a moment, but he thought he saw a chance of putting right his previous blunder by producing a disciple, or perhaps a former disciple, of Jesus. He made up his mind.

'Wait here,' he said and hurried back to the inner room.

Annas, Caiaphas and the priests were still debating. One of the priests who had listened to Jesus in the temple said he had made inquiries in Bethany, and it might be possible to seize Jesus in the house of Lazarus, but at once another said that this was too dangerous, for the Bethany people were his strongest supporters. They were interrupted by the entry of Malchus, and Caiaphas impatiently asked him his business.

'My lord,' said Malchus, his voice rising with excitement, 'there is a man outside, wishes to speak with you.'

'We are not to be disturbed,' said Caiaphas frigidly. But when Malchus said that he was one of the twelve who came from Galilee with Jesus of Nazareth, the gathering was immediately alert. Annas and Caiaphas exchanged a meaning glance. Malchus was ordered to bring the man in, and Caiaphas said as he went, 'This might well be the answer we are looking for.'

The priests waited in silence for Malchus' return, and when he entered he stood aside to let the man pass. He came in slowly, hesitatingly, and for a moment was dazzled by the light after the gloom of the courtyard. He looked round at the expectant faces, and then turned back to the door. Malchus stepped quickly behind him, barring the way.

'You may go, captain,' said the high priest, and then he spoke to the stranger gently. 'You wished to see me, friend?' The man nodded. 'What is your name?'

'Judas Iscariot.'

PART 8

Behold the Man

In ANOTHER, lowlier part of the city the disciples were making their way by twos and threes to a certain house where Jesus awaited them. The upper room where they met was bare of ornaments or hangings, and furnished only with couches and a low table. In one corner stood a pitcher of water, a bowl and a towel. On the table the Passover supper was laid, including the loaf of flat, unleavened bread, jugs of wine and some cups. Some of the disciples sat down, some stood in groups, talking animatedly, although most of them were tired and dusty from walking.

James and Andrew had had difficulty in finding the way. Andrew explained that James had thought they were being followed, so they had walked right to the top of the city to shake the fellow off. Presently Thaddeus and James Alphaeus arrived, and John, counting them all, said that made eleven, and only one was missing. That was Judas.

James sat down to ease his feet. 'What made you choose this place, Peter?' he asked.

'We didn't choose it,' replied Peter. 'The master did. Just told us to come to this part of the town and look for a man carrying a pitcher of water. Well, he wasn't hard to spot among all the women at the well, so we followed him here and gave him the master's message about preparing a room for the Passover meal.'

'I see,' said James, and added, 'And where's the man with the pitcher of water now?'

Peter wondered at his question, and James went on to ask why the man had not provided a servant with water to wash their feet, for the streets were filthy, and even his stairs none too clean. But John said placatingly that he was a poor man, with no servant, and that they would just have to make the best of it. Everything else was prepared: the meat and the sauces, the bread and the wine.

They chatted together, Peter recalling their *first* supper with the master, when there were only four of them; and Andrew remembered that Jesus had told them of the Kingdom growing secretly like leaven in bread, and how he and James had been disappointed, because they had expected a Kingdom of power and glory.

'Perhaps after to-night,' said John, 'there'll be no more secrecy. I think something's going to happen to-night, and that the glory of the Kingdom may be very near.'

Matthew had joined them. 'I don't like to look ahead,' he said. 'The present's good enough for me. "Give us this day our daily bread." That's the part of our prayer I like best,' and he sat down with a sigh.

'All the same, we've got to be prepared, Matthew,' returned Peter, sitting beside him. 'The Kingdom won't come without a struggle. Remember what the master said: "I did not come to bring peace but a sword"? Well, I'm ready to fight for the Kingdom if needs be. Andrew and I have brought swords.'

'Who's talking about swords?' asked Philip, and Nathaniel explained that Simon Peter and John thought something was going to happen that night. Perhaps that was why the master had told them to come separately, and to take care they were not followed.

'I don't see why we couldn't have stayed in Bethany,' said Thomas, grumbling a bit. 'Are we going back there to-night?'

But Philip thought not, and that they would go to Gethsemane again. Meanwhile Judas had at last come in, and John welcomed him, and suggested that they should both go and sit next to Jesus.

'I must bathe my feet first,' said Judas. 'Is there a servant here?'

'No, I'm sorry there isn't,' said John. 'There's water over there but nobody to pour it. I shouldn't bother, Judas. None of us has.' He and Judas moved over to the table where Jesus was standing and took their places on either side of him, and James noted angrily that Judas who had come last had taken the best place. Jesus called to him.

'James.'

'Master?'

'Tell me, who is greater, the man who sits at table or the man who serves him?'

'Why,' said James in surprise, 'he that sits at table.'

'Yet I am here among you as your servant.' Jesus took off his robe and, fetching the pitcher of water, the bowl and the towel, he knelt by each of his disciples in turn and washed the dust and dirt from their feet. When he came to Simon Peter, Peter protested.

'Lord, is it for you to wash my feet?'

'What I am doing you do not understand now. But soon you will understand.'

'Master, I will never let you wash my feet.'

'If you do not let me wash you, Simon, it means that you have no part in me or in my work.'

'No part in you?' asked Peter. 'Then, Lord wash not only my feet but my hands and head too.'

Jesus smiled. 'But you have bathed already, Simon Peter,' he said. 'A man that has bathed does not need to do more than wash the stains from his feet. Now the whole body is clean. All of you are clean. No, not all.' He had met Judas' eye, and spoke gently. 'Judas, let me wash the stains from your feet.'

Slowly and reluctantly Judas presented his feet to be washed and dried, and when it was done he said, with a touch of cynicism, 'Thank you, master.'

'Do you understand what it is I have done for you?' asked Jesus.

'Yes, Lord.'

'You hail me as Master and Lord, and rightly. That is what I am. Why, then if I have washed your feet, I, who am the Master and the Lord, you in your turn should wash one another's feet. Do you understand what I am saying to you?'

They all murmured 'Yes,' except Judas, who was silent.

Jesus and the disciples returned to the table, and James asked forgiveness for any ambitious thoughts he had had, but Jesus comforted him. 'I know the men I have chosen,' he said. 'But the scripture says, "Yea, mine own familiar friend in whom I trusted, who did eat of my bread, hath lifted up his heel against me."' Then, showing great distress, he said 'Indeed and indeed I say to you that one of you will betray me.'

There was consternation among the disciples, and they looked at each other with suspicion. And at once each in turn begged to be told if *he* were the one. All but Judas, who still was silent.

'It is one of the twelve who dips his hand in the dish with me,' said Jesus, and they questioned among themselves, asking if Jesus could mean that one of them would desert him, for betrayal was unthinkable. Back and forth they went over the words, shocked by what Jesus had said.

Then Judas took a piece of bread and made to dip it in the bowl, but Jesus took it from him, and dipped it for him.

'Lord, is it I?' asked Judas quietly, looking directly at Jesus, who replied, 'You have said so. . . . What you have to do, do quickly.'

Judas ate the bread, rose from the table, and went from the room.

One or two of the disciples noticed his going, but supposed that Jesus had sent him on an errand, and none guessed that Judas had gone to betray his master.

When the sound of Judas' footfalls died away on the stairs, Jesus began to speak to the remaining eleven disciples.

'Children,' he said, 'I have longed with all my heart to eat this Passover meal with you before I suffer, for I tell you I shall not eat it again until the day of its fulfilment in the Kingdom of God.'

'Is the Kingdom so near, then, master?' asked James eagerly.

'The hour is very near when the Son of Man shall be glorified,' was the reply.

'And what of us, master?' questioned James.

'You are the men who have kept to my side in my temptations and hours of trial, and as my Father has given to me a Kingdom, so do I give to you a place to eat and drink at my table in my Kingdom.'

Jesus took the flat, dry loaf of unleavened bread, and the disciples were silent while he blessed it: 'Thanks be to Thee, O Lord

God, King of the world, who bringest forth bread from the earth.
Amen.'

'Amen,' they murmured.

Jesus broke the bread, saying, 'Take and eat. This is my body
which is given for you. Do this in remembrance of me.'

With puzzled, anxious faces they each took a piece of the bread
and ate it as the platter was handed round, and each was filled with
fear and foreboding.

Then John poured out a cup of wine, and handed it to Jesus, asking him to bless it, which he did, saying, 'Thanks be to Thee, O
Lord God, for this the fruit of the vine. Amen,' and again the disciples echoed, 'Amen.'

'Drink, all of you, of this,' said Jesus, handing the cup to John.
'For this is my blood of the New Covenant which is poured out for
you and for many, for the forgiveness of sins.'

John, trying to get back to the more ordinary, familiar Passover,
asked him whether he would not drink first, but Jesus answered,
'Take it and share it among yourselves, for I shall drink no more of
the fruit of the vine until the Kingdom of God is come.'

The cup was passed from hand to hand, and they all drank. John,
who was very afraid now, leaned close to Jesus and asked what this
meant.

'I am the true vine,' said Jesus, 'and you are the branches, and it
is my Father who tends the vine. Every branch in me that bears
no fruit, he cuts away, and every fruitful branch He trims clean so
that it yields more fruit. You, through the teaching I have given
you, are clean already. You have only to live on in me and I will
live on in you. Just as the branch alone can bear no fruit but must
stay in the vine, so can you bear no fruit unless you stay in me.'

But this was beyond John's understanding. 'Lord,' he said, 'you
know we will stay with you always.'

'My children,' went on Jesus, 'it is only a short time now that
we have together, and where I am going you cannot come. And so
I give to you a new commandment—love one another. Love one
another as I loved you. It is by the love you show for one another
that men will know you are my disciples.'

'Lord,' cried Peter in agony, 'where are you going?'

'I am going where you cannot follow me now; but you shall follow me afterwards,' was the reply. 'Do not let your heart be troubled. Have faith in God; have faith in me. There are many rooms in my Father's house, and I go to prepare a place for you, so that where I am you may be also.' He looked around at their troubled faces. 'Do not be afraid; you know where I am going, and you know the way there.'

'But, Lord,' protested Thomas, 'we do *not* know where you are going. How can we know the way?'

'I am the Way,' said Jesus, 'and the Truth and the Life. No one comes to the Father but through me. From now on you will know the Father, for you have seen Him.'

'Lord, show us the Father—that is all we ask,' entreated Philip.

'Have I been so long with you, and still you do not know me, Philip?' asked Jesus gently. 'He that has seen me has seen the Father. The words I speak to you, and the works you have seen me do, come not from me but from God who dwells within me. Indeed I tell you, he that has faith in me shall himself do the things I do, and greater works also shall he do. Whatsoever you shall ask in my name I will do it, for even as the Father has loved me, so I have loved you. Stay in my love.'

'Lord, you know that we love you,' said John.

'If you love me you will keep my commandment,' urged Jesus. 'Love one another even as I have loved you.'

He paused a moment, and the disciples watched him. Then he continued firmly and yet gently: 'The greatest love that a man can show is to lay down his life for his friends.'

There was another pause, and slowly it began to be clear to the disciples that Jesus was to die.

'You are my friends,' he continued, 'for all the things that I heard from my Father I have made known to you. Now, I go to my Father, but I will not leave you alone. I will ask the Father and He will send you a Comforter, the Spirit of Truth, to abide with you for ever.' Silently they listened, hanging on to every word—trying to understand. 'I have many more things to say to you, but you cannot bear them now, so this Holy Spirit whom the Father will send in my name will guide you into the truth and bring to your remembrance all that I have said to you. I leave you peace. Not peace as the world knows it, but my peace I give unto you. Let not your heart be troubled, neither let it be afraid.'

He rose to his feet.

'I can talk no longer with you, for the Prince of this world is on his way, and as the Father has commanded me, so must I do.'

'Where are we going, master? To Gethsemane?' asked John, and Jesus said, yes, they were going to Gethsemane, but first they would pray together. All the disciples stood up, while he prayed: 'Father, the hour has come. Glorify Thy son, that Thy son may glorify thee. I have finished the task on earth that Thou gavest me, and made Thy Holy Name known to these men Thou gavest me from the world.

'Now that I come to you, Holy Father, I pray Thee to keep and guard them, not to take them from the world but to guard them from evil. And I pray also for all those who are brought by their teaching to have faith in me, that they may be one, even as Thou, Father, and I are one. So that the love Thou hast for me may be in them. Amen.'

'Amen,' said the disciples. Then one of them started the Passover hymn, and they sang it together to the end.

When they had sung the hymn they went out and walked together to the Mount of Olives, and came to the garden called Gethsemane. Here Jesus told them to stay and watch, but they were anxious for him, and begged him to stay and not forsake them.

'I will not forsake you, little flock,' said Jesus, 'though all of you will desert me to-night.' As the disciples protested, he went on quickly, 'Is it not written, "I will smite the shepherd and the sheep of the flock will be scattered"? But do not be afraid, for when I am risen, I will find my flock again and go on before you into Galilee.'

'Master,' cried the impetuous Peter, 'even though all the rest should desert you, I never will,' and Jesus replied, 'Simon, Simon, Satan is trying to claim you all for his own, so that he can sift you apart as a man sifts wheat. But I prayed for you, Simon, that your faith will not fail you for ever, and when you have come back to me, strengthen your brothers.'

'But, Lord,' protested Peter, 'I am ready to go anywhere with you, even though it be to prison or to death.'

'I tell you, Peter,' replied Jesus, 'before the cock crows you will, three times, deny that you know me.'

Peter was vehement in his reply. 'Deny you, master? No, not me. I will die with you first.'

And he was echoed by James and Andrew who declared that they would never desert Jesus, but that they would fight for the Kingdom and die for it if they must—that they'd fight to the death, even though they had only got two swords.

'It is enough,' said Jesus. Then he told eight of them to stay and rest awhile, while he went on with Peter, James and John.

As the four of them walked among the olive trees, John noticed that Jesus was in deep distress. Presently he stopped, and for a moment covered his face with his hands.

'Lord!' cried John, hardly able to bear his master's suffering. Jesus raised his head. 'My heart is very heavy,' he said, and then, to these three men who had been his closest friends, 'keep near me and stay awake while I pray.'

Silently they watched as Jesus walked a little way from them and knelt to pray. Then the three of them sat down on the ground and pulled their coats around them, for the night was cool. For a long while Jesus knelt there in the quiet garden wrestling with his sorrow, and praying to God. In his agony he prayed, 'Father, all things are possible to Thee. If Thou be willing, take this cup from me. Nevertheless, not my will but Thine be done.' At last he rose and went back to his three disciples to find them sleeping. He put a hand on Peter's shoulder to wake him, asking, 'Simon, are you sleeping? Had you not strength to watch one hour with me?'

Peter woke at once, and he was bitterly ashamed. 'Master,' he said, 'forgive me. I meant to stay awake.' And the other two heard him and woke too, in distress at their weakness.

'Watch and pray that you are not led into temptation,' said Jesus. 'The spirit indeed is willing but the flesh is weak. The flesh is weak,' he repeated, almost to himself; 'I must pray again to the Father.' And though they begged him not to leave them, he moved away from them and again he knelt to pray. And after he had prayed he came back to his disciples to find they had once more fallen asleep.

For the third time Jesus prayed alone saying, 'My Father, if this cup may not pass away from me, but I must drink it, Thy will be done.'

Once more he returned, and once more they were fast asleep, but this time Jesus only looked down on them as they slept and said gently, 'Sleep on, then, and take your rest.'

But a moment later the sleeping men were roused by frightened cries from the eight disciples who were a little distance away. There was a tramp of feet through the darkness, and the voices of the disciples calling, 'Who are you? Where are you going?' And then, more urgently as they suspected what men these were, 'Peter—John, warn the master!'

'The hour has come,' said Jesus. 'Rise up now for my betrayer is close at hand.'

The three disciples struggled to their feet, as the tramping feet drew nearer. And now they saw men with torches coming through the trees. Among them, although they could not yet see him, was Judas, guiding Malchus and the temple guards to Jesus.

'Your man is the one I kiss,' said Judas in an undertone. 'Arrest him, and take him safely away.' He was sure of himself now, and there was no going back.

The three disciples gathered about Jesus as if to protect him, and Peter put his hand on his sword; but James called suddenly, 'It's all right. It's all right, master; Judas is with them.'

Judas came forward through the darkness in the flickering light of the torches. He stopped for a second and looked at Jesus, then stepped towards him.

'Friend, what is your errand?' asked Jesus.

'Greetings, master,' said Judas, and he embraced Jesus, and kissed him.

'Judas, do you betray the Son of Man with a kiss?' asked Jesus.

At once the guards surrounded them. Peter drew his sword, but Jesus stopped him, and said, 'If I am the man you are looking for, let these others go free.'

He turned to face the guards, some of them armed with sticks, others with swords, and as Malchus came near to seize Jesus, Peter lunged forward with his sword and struck at his ear, wounding it.

Gethsemane

'Simon, are you sleeping?'

Judas Iscariot

'Don't dare to lay hands on him,' he cried, but the guards held fast to Jesus' arms. Malchus fell to his knees with a cry of pain.

'Put up your sword, Peter,' said Jesus. Then he asked the soldiers to release him for a moment. When they did so, keeping suspicious watch on him, Jesus stepped forward to Malchus and touched his injured ear, saying, 'It is well again.' Then he turned to the mob. 'I see you have come out with swords and sticks to capture me as though I were a robber. Yet day after day I was with you in the temple and you did not lay hands on me.'

'Bring him along,' said a commanding voice, and the soldiers seized him again and marched him off. The three disciples made to follow him, Peter drawing his sword again, but the mob turned on them angrily, 'Any more of that and you'll all be arrested.'

At this threat the disciples gave up the attempt to follow Jesus, and fled into the darkness—all but Peter, who watched him go, and then followed him afar off.

From the Mount of Olives they took Jesus to Caiaphas, the high priest, with whom the scribes and elders were assembled. And while they questioned him two of the temple guards waited in the court-yard, warming themselves at a brazier fire and talking to two women servants. One of the women was chaffing the guards, say-ing it took a lot of them to capture one man, and that she'd been busy all evening with people coming and going and asking for some-thing to eat because they had been sent out by Lord Caiaphas in the middle of the night to capture a dangerous criminal. She laughed. 'Dangerous criminal indeed, looked as meek as a lamb to me.'

One of the guards defended himself indignantly. How were they to know, he asked, that there'd be only one of them? Jesus had eleven men with him, some of them armed, but they were a cowardly lot, and every one of them ran away when their leader was arrested.

No one noticed Peter who stood by the gate listening—hoping for a chance to get near to Jesus.

Another guard, who was Malchus' brother, spoke up. 'He may *look* as meek as a lamb,' he said, 'but he must be a pretty dangerous fellow, else why would Caiaphas call members of the council to hold a trial in the middle of the night?'

'Want to get it over before the Sabbath, I suppose,' suggested the first guard. 'Is the prisoner in there now?'

'Yes,' said the other. 'Malchus and me took him in. We listened for a bit outside until it got too cold. They didn't seem to be getting anywhere. The prisoner just stood there not speaking, and the witnesses didn't seem too sure of their evidence.'

'Who's that standing over there in the cold?' asked one of the servant girls, who had just noticed Peter. She moved over to him, and asked him if he would like to come and warm himself by the fire. Startled, he found he was unable to speak.

'Why, you're trembling!' she said. 'It's all right, nobody'll hurt you. You've got a sword, I see. Don't worry,' she added, as Peter attempted to hide it, 'there's plenty with sticks and swords to-night. Were you one of them that went to Gethsemane?' And while he struggled to find words, she went on, 'Well, come along in, anyway. You'll be quite welcome.' Then she laughed as she added, 'as long as you're not a follower of that Jesus.' She put her face close to his. 'You're not, are you?'

'No, no, of course not,' stammered Peter. The girl led him over to the fire, where the soldiers stood talking.

'Where's Malchus now?' asked one of the guard, and his brother said he had gone to bed.

'Still nursing his ear?' asked the woman sarcastically. 'He asked me to look at it, said it had been cut off or something—it looked as good as the other one to me.'

'Mind what you're saying—Malchus is my brother,' said the guard. 'One of those mad Galileans *did* strike at his ear with a sword.'

'Well, why didn't you arrest him?' asked the girl pertly.

'He ran away like all the others,' said the young guard. 'But if I ever see him again I'll give him a taste of my sword.'

Peter, terrified, turned his back and kept his face in shadow.

'You'll not see him again,' said the woman. 'He's probably on his way back to Galilee by now,' and they all laughed.

The girl again pressed Peter to come near the fire. Peter mumbled his thanks and then, looking towards the entrance, asked nervously, 'Is that—is that where the prisoner is?' The girl nodded.

There was a sudden hush and the woman, coming over to Peter, said, 'Talking of Galilee, that's where you're from, judging by your accent. Tell us, did you know this Jesus of Nazareth?'

'No,' said Peter, his nerve going. 'I don't know the man.' The guards had drawn closer to Peter now, and he was nervous of their nearness.

'Just a minute,' said Malchus' brother aggressively, 'just a minute. I believe you're one of his disciples. Didn't I see you in the garden?'

'For the love of God leave me alone,' cried Peter, and now he was really terrified. 'I tell you I don't know the man.'

A cock crew as he spoke, and, sick at heart, Peter remembered Jesus' words, 'Before the cock crows you will deny me three times.' He turned to the doorway, and at this moment Jesus came out from the council chamber. His hands were tied, and he was accompanied by two priests, who beckoned to the guards to take Jesus away. As he was led past the fire, Jesus turned and looked at Peter. Then the party moved off and out of the courtyard.

Peter was left alone by the fire. He stumbled across the courtyard to the gate where he had come in, and after one last look towards his master he turned his face to the wall and wept bitterly.

It was still early morning when Caiaphas and the two priests left the house, followed by the guards leading Jesus. The town was just waking to life, and a woman coming out of a doorway with her water-jar looked after them without much interest. Once more the cock crowed.

Under the sign of the Roman eagle a sentry stood on duty outside the palace of Pontius Pilate, the Governor. Through a gateway another soldier led Caiaphas and two other priests, and left them to wait by the great chair, known as 'The Seat of Judgment.'

'What are those Jews doing here so early?' asked the sentry as the soldier passed him.

'That one in the middle is Caiaphas, the high priest—brought a prisoner to be tried by the Governor,' explained the soldier briefly. 'Wants the death sentence.'

The sentry whistled. 'Not another crucifixion! We've got three to-day already. We'll have to get another cross made if there's going to be four.'

'Who are the others?' asked the soldier.

'Oh, two common thieves,' was the answer; 'I don't know their names, and that fellow Barabbas who killed a man in one of those nationalist brawls. What's this prisoner done?'

'I don't know,' said the soldier, 'some mysterious religious crime, I suppose, since the high priest brought him.'

Caiaphas and his priests had watched with impatience as the two men gossiped in the doorway, and now one of the priests was sent over to interrupt them. 'I beg you to make haste,' he said, 'to inform the Governor that we are here. Our business is urgent.'

The soldier turned and looked at him, then with a shrug made a move to go. The sentry settled down at his post. 'Getting the Governor up at this hour. What's the hurry?'

'That's another part of their religion,' replied the soldier, with a grin. 'To-morrow's the Sabbath. No killing on the Sabbath. Get it over the day before.' And he laughed as he went out. 'These Jews!' muttered the sentry.

Meanwhile Caiaphas was giving last instructions to the three priests while they waited for Pilate. He held a charge sheet in his hand.

'Now remember,' said Caiaphas, 'there is no need for us to mention the charge of blasphemy. We can merely state that according to our law Jesus is guilty and deserves the death penalty. If the Governor presses us for details of the charge then we point to this,' and he tapped the charge sheet, 'that Jesus has been calling himself a king, that he taught in the temple that the people should not pay taxes to Caesar.'

'Will Pilate order a new trial?' asked one of the priests. But Caiaphas thought this was unlikely, and that Pilate would take their word.

'Suppose,' the second priest suggested, 'he refuses to condemn Jesus—or suppose the people demand his release. It is the custom every Passover to release one prisoner.'

Caiaphas pointed out that the people did not yet know that he had been arrested, so they could not demand his release, and then the first priest had a brilliant idea.

'Barabbas is a popular man,' he said. 'He's due to die to-day—I heard the soldier say so. It wouldn't take much to stir up the people to demand Barabbas.' But Caiaphas hushed him, for the Governor was approaching.

Pilate entered. He was about forty, a soldierly man, impatient, loyal, tactless, but with a true sense of justice. He had on several occasions blundered in his duty by offending the Jews unnecessarily. He was rather annoyed now at being called at this early hour, and, after a cold look at the priests, he walked straight to his chair and sat down.

'Well, my lord high priest,' he said briskly, 'I understand you have brought a prisoner to be tried. What is the charge against him?'

'No need to try him, Excellency,' said Caiaphas, very carefully playing for time. 'He has been tried already by our court, and he is guilty. If it were not so we should not have brought him to you.'

'Very well,' said Pilate, matching strategy with strategy. 'Take him yourselves and judge him according to your law.'

'With respect, Excellency,' pointed out Caiaphas, 'I would remind you that it is not lawful for us to put any man to death.'

'Death?' asked Pilate. 'You have found him deserving of death?' When the priests nodded, he asked sharply, 'Upon what charge?'

Caiaphas was ready for this. 'Sir,' he said, 'we have found this man, Jesus of Nazareth is his name, perverting our nation, forbidding the payment of tribute to Caesar, and calling himself the Messiah, the Christ.'

' "Messiah," "Christ,"—what do these words mean?' asked Pilate impatiently, and again Caiaphas was ready with his answer. 'They mean "The King," ' he said deliberately.

Pilate was astonished. 'The King?' he repeated. 'The King of the Jews?'

Caiaphas nodded, glad to have made an impression. Then Pilate with a motion of his hand signalled to Caiaphas and the priests to step aside; and he called to the soldiers by the door to bring the prisoner in.

They waited—the priests with anxiety, Pilate with some curiosity. Presently Jesus was brought in by two soldiers. His hands were still bound, and when the soldiers had led him to the judgment seat, Pilate signalled to them to return to their post at the door, then stared at Jesus—a long, incredulous look.

'Are *you* King of the Jews?' he asked.

'Do *you* ask me this?' returned Jesus, in a low voice. 'Or have these others said it of me?'

'Am I a Jew?' asked Pilate scornfully. 'It is your own nation and its chief priests who have brought you before me. What have you done?' When Jesus did not answer, he asked: 'Are you a king?'

'My Kingdom is not of this world,' said Jesus. 'If it were my servants would fight to save me from my enemies. But no, my Kingdom is not here.'

'So you are a king then?' said Pilate again, and was puzzled by Jesus' reply: 'It is you that say I am a king. I was born and came into the world to bear witness to the truth. Everyone that would know and accept the truth listens to my voice.'

'The truth?' queried Pilate looking hard at Jesus. 'What is truth?' but without waiting for an answer he motioned for the priests to come forward.

'You have brought this man before me,' he said to them, 'as one that has perverted the people from their allegiance to Rome. I have examined him, and find him not guilty of the charge you make.'

'Not guilty?' exclaimed Caiaphas, coldly furious and beginning to lose his temper. 'He may appear meek and harmless before you, Excellency, but we have witnesses who heard him threaten to pull down the temple.'

The first priest could scarcely wait to get in his word. 'Others saw him walking through the temple thrashing innocent people with a whip!'

'With my own ears,' declared the second priest, 'I heard him urging the people to render no tribute to Caesar.'

Pilate listened with obvious distaste to this outburst, then turned to Jesus. 'You hear how many crimes they accuse you of? Have you nothing to say?' When Jesus remained silent, he turned to the priests again. 'None of these charges you make render the prisoner deserving of death.'

'Does not treason deserve death?' asked Caiaphas.

'I find him not guilty of treason.'

'Why, he calls himself a king. Anyone who does that speaks against Caesar.'

If Pilate was slightly perturbed, he hid behind his frigid bearing. 'As Caesar's representative,' he said icily, 'you will allow me to decide what is treason and what is not.' As the priests began

'Judas, do you betray the Son of Man with a kiss?'

Peter denies the master

Jesus before Pilate

to murmur angrily, he added, 'If you still demand punishment on the other charges, I will have him flogged, and then release him.'

'You cannot release him,' exclaimed Caiaphas, white with fury.

'Indeed I can,' replied Pilate. 'It is the custom that one prisoner is released at your Passover time. I shall release Jesus, the King of the Jews.' He called to the soldiers. 'Take the prisoner away.'

'To be flogged, sir?' asked the soldier woodenly.

'Yes,' said Pilate, looking away from Jesus.

Jesus was led away. In the courtyard below a crowd was beginning to collect, and one of the priests moved to the window and looked down.

'What is that noise?' asked Pilate irritably, and was told that the people were gathering outside—to welcome Barabbas, the prisoner they expected to be released. There was triumph in the priest's voice as he said this—as if he and Caiaphas had brought out a trump card.

'Barabbas is a thief and a murderer,' retorted Pilate, to which Caiaphas replied that Jesus was a blasphemer and a traitor.

'Enough!' said Pilate curtly, but Caiaphas was determined to the last.

'According to our law he deserves to die,' he said, 'because he claims to be the Son of God.'

Pilate paused for a moment, irresolute, then he matched Caiaphas' determination with his own. 'I have told you my decision,' he said. 'You may go.'

Left alone he stood thinking for a time, troubled in mind. 'The son of a god?' he said to himself softly. 'What god?' Then he walked over to the door and listened, wincing as he heard the sound of the lash on Jesus' back.

'Eight—nine—ten,' counted a soldier's voice between each stroke. 'Have you had enough, your Majesty?' and the other soldiers joined in the laughter.

'Here, King Jesus,' said another voice, 'here's a crown for you—made of the very finest thorns.'

'Give it here,' said the first soldier, and was warned to mind his hand—the thorns were sharp.

'Ow—ye gods,' said the other. 'Rather your head than mine, your Majesty. I hereby crown you King of the Jews.'

There was a gasp from some of the soldiers as the crown was pressed down on Jesus' head. 'Have a heart. No need to press it down.'

'He likes his crown to fit, don't you, your Majesty?'

Pilate winced as he watched, and did not notice the centurion who had come in and now stood beside him.

'Your Excellency.'

Pilate turned on him with a start.

'What do you want?'

'I bring a message, Excellency, from the Lady Claudia.'

'Well?' asked Pilate, frowning, but the centurion hesitated. 'Well, what is my wife's message?'

'She told me to say this to you, sir. "Do nothing to that innocent man, for I have suffered much this night in a dream about him."'

'In a dream?' echoed Pilate, almost to himself. 'So was Julius Caesar warned by his wife's dream. . . . "Do nothing to that innocent man"—the Son of God?' Then he turned to the centurion. 'Tell my guards to bring the prisoner here.'

While the centurion went to obey him, Pilate crossed to the window and looked down for a moment on to the crowds who were growing noisier. From time to time a cry of 'We want Barabbas' was heard. Pilate, deeply troubled, turned and went back to his judgment seat, waiting.

A moment later the soldiers came in, leading Jesus. Pilate stared at him. He was now dressed in a purple robe which the soldiers had thrown over his lacerated shoulders. On his head was the crown of thorns, and blood ran from his forehead; but in spite of the pain he stood calm and erect. Pilate watched him, and fear crept into his heart, lest there was something supernatural about this man. But he pulled himself together, and commanded Jesus to come near, motioning to the soldiers to stay where they were. As Jesus stood in front of him, Pilate searched his face, trying to reconcile his idea of 'a god' with this suffering, blood-stained figure.

'Jesus, tell me who you are and where you came from,' said Pilate, but there was no answer.

'What? Will you not answer me?' continued Pilate. 'Don't you know that I have the power to release you or power to crucify you?'

Jesus replied, 'You would have no power over me at all if it had not

been given you from above. It is those who delivered me to you who
bear the guilt.'

Before Pilate could reply, the roar of the crowd outside became
louder, the cry of 'We want Barabbas' coming as a sort of chant.
Mustering all his resolution, Pilate crossed to the window and
stepped out on to the balcony. The roar swelled to a cheer as the
crowd caught sight of him. He looked down on them. The two
priests were in front of the crowd, and leading the cheers were
some of the temple guards put there among the people for the
purpose.

Pilate raised his arms to quieten the crowd.

'My lord priests and men of Jerusalem,' he said. 'To-day as is
the custom at your Passover festival, I shall release to you a prisoner.'

'We want Barabbas,' yelled a voice, leading the crowd to yell with
him.

But Pilate hushed them, and pressed on. 'I hold another prisoner
here,' he said, signing to the soldiers to bring Jesus out on the balcony. 'Behold the man.'

There was silence, broken only by a woman's scream. Most of the
people were astonished to see Jesus there, for news that he was a
prisoner had not reached them. There were exclamations on every
side. What had happened? Why was Jesus the prophet a prisoner—
he never did any harm? When was he arrested? At a sign from the
priests, the 'cheer-leaders' started another cry, 'Crucify him.' There
was a moment of shocked silence then the clamour broke out again.
'No, no,' cried other voices, 'release Jesus. Let Jesus go.'

Pilate let them go on shouting for a while, and then with Jesus
standing beside him, he checked them.

'Shall I release unto you Jesus—the King of the Jews?' he asked.

'Yes,' shouted the crowd. 'Give us Jesus. Let Jesus go,' but they
were soon drowned by other, better organized shouts of 'We want
Barabbas. Give us Barabbas,' and before long the calls for Jesus
died down, and shouts of 'Barabbas' filled the air.

Pilate quelled the noise with a gesture, and called, 'What then
shall I do with Jesus, whom you call Christ?'

'Crucify him!'

'Why? What wrong has he done?'

'Crucify him.'

'What, shall I crucify your King?'

There was a confused murmur from the crowd, and some hesitation, but quickly one of the priests called out, 'We have no King but Caesar,' and another priest added, 'If you release this man you are not Caesar's friend.'

The crowd began again: 'Crucify him. Crucify him,' they shouted with increasing fervour.

Pilate turned to a soldier and asked him to bring a bowl of water, then once more he spoke to the crowd. 'Listen to me,' he said, and another soldier called, 'Silence for the Governor.'

The clamour died down, and there was silence.

'Listen to me, people of Jewry,' said Pilate. 'I find no fault with this man. It is you who would crucify him.'

A boy brought a bowl of water and put it before him.

'See now,' continued Pilate, 'I wash my hands of all responsibility and am innocent of the blood of this good man.'

Led by the priests and leaders the crowd answered, 'His blood be upon us and upon our children.'

'Release Barabbas,' commanded Pilate. Pilate tried to avoid Jesus' eye but could not, as he turned and went into the house. Then, with rough hands and little courtesy, the soldiers hustled Jesus off.

Outside, the crowd began to disperse and as the priests gathered together and talked of their success, Judas, who had been one of the crowd, rushed to them holding out the bag of silver which they had paid him for betraying Jesus.

His face was haggard, and he spoke wildly. 'I have sinned. I have sinned. I have betrayed innocent blood.' He flung the purse of silver at their feet. 'Take back your filthy money.'

The priests looked at him coldly and turned away. At that moment two Roman soldiers passed carrying an enormous wooden cross with a sign nailed to the top of it, 'Barabbas, Thief and Murderer.' With a cry, Judas rushed at them, and flung himself upon the cross—'You shall not kill him—you shall not crucify my lord.'

'Hands off,' said the nearest soldier roughly. He lowered the bottom end of the cross to the ground, and the two of them leaned it against the wall. Then they seized Judas and flung him away.

Pilate was writing the inscription on the sign to be nailed to Jesus' cross. He finished the last letter, and handed the inscription to the waiting priests. Caiaphas took it and read it: 'Jesus of Nazareth, the King of the Jews.'

'Excellency,' he remonstrated, 'the wording is wrong. The charge should read, "He said he was the King of the Jews."'

'What I have written, I have written,' said Pilate, dismissing them.

Once outside Caiaphas handed the sign to a soldier, who carried it to the street, to where the huge cross was leaning against the wall. The inscription intended for Barabbas was ripped off, the new one nailed in its place, and passers-by read it: 'Jesus of Nazareth, the King of the Jews.'

So Jesus was delivered to be crucified. And when they had mocked him, they took off from him the purple robe and put on him his own garments, and led him away to crucify him.

PART 9

'I Am With You Always'

AFTER Pilate had delivered Jesus to be crucified, they took him from the city to a place called Golgotha, which means 'the place of the skull.' It was called this because the caves at the base of this small, round hill gave the appearance of eyes in a skull.

On the top of the hill stood two crosses, and on them hung the two thieves. Although it was early in the morning crowds had gathered and were staring up, some with horror and pity, some with callous indifference, at the men on the crosses.

'Well, there's two robbers in the right place,' said one, and he called up at them tauntingly, 'How's it feel up there?'

'Oh, it's cruel—cruel,' said a woman, shuddering, 'I wish I'd never come.'

'They don't feel nothing, more's the pity,' said another man, and the first agreed that such men had no decent feelings.

A stranger pushed past them to get a better view, and asked why there were only two crosses. He'd heard there were three criminals to be crucified. He was told that the third was even then being nailed to a cross.

'Who is it?' he asked.

'Haven't you heard? It's that man, Jesus of Nazareth.'

'What, him they called Messiah?'

'*I am innocent of the blood of this good man*'

Golgotha

Casting lots

'That's right. That's what they've written on his cross: "Jesus of Nazareth, King of the Jews." '

There was laughter at this, and when it died down the stranger asked what Jesus was to be crucified for. 'The priests got him,' was the reply.

'Fancy handing him over to the Romans though,' said the stranger, and someone said, 'Oh, you know what the priests are, hand in glove with Rome.'

Over and above the chatter of the crowd came the relentless hammering of a mallet on iron nails. 'It's cruel, wicked,' cried the woman who had protested earlier. 'He was a *good* man.'

'A *good* man? *Him?* He was a blasphemer—a traitor—an enemy of the people.'

'Jesus an enemy? He was the friend of the poor.'

'Yes. That's why the priests got him. He was a traitor, a friend of Rome.'

'How could he be a friend of Rome? It's the Romans nailing him to the cross now.'

There were others joining in the argument now, some saying he was a madman, possessed of a devil, calling himself the Son of God and King of the Jews, while others defended him, saying he had meant no harm and did not deserve to die; but they were suddenly hushed as the hammering gave way to a creaking noise. There were strained shouts from the soldiers. 'Steady'—'Steady'—'Heave' —'Hold it—and drop' as the third cross, the cross of Jesus, was hauled up and, with a dull thud, lowered into the hole prepared for it. And out of the silence came the voice of the man on the cross.

'Father, forgive them for they know not what they do.'

The babble of cries and shouts broke out again as the crowd surged forward.

'Keep back,' shouted a soldier. 'You can't go nearer than this.' Then he turned to a group of three people, two women and a man who stood silently staring up at the cross. 'Here's your wine and myrrh, lady,' he said to the older woman. 'I offered it to your friend, but he wouldn't take it.' But Mary did not hear—her eyes were fixed on her son. Mary Magdalene covered her face with her hands, the disciple John cried, 'Master!' but Mary the mother

stretched out her arms as though she would lift her son down from
his cross.

The morning grew hotter as the sun rose higher. In front of the
three crosses, four soldiers settled down to wait for the crucified
men to die. Three sat on the ground playing dice to pass the time,
and the fourth joined them. He was carrying a bundle. It was the
clothes of the three prisoners, by custom the property of the
soldiers on duty. They set about sorting them.

'Nothing much here,' said one, and the others agreed, saying
they were only fit for rags, and that if they had to be thieves, it was
a pity they couldn't have stolen some good clothes. However, they
divided the clothes among themselves: three head scarves, a sash,
three pairs of sandals and a knife, two cloaks and two tunics.

'That leaves one white robe between the four of us,' said one
soldier.

'Rip it into four,' said another, offering the knife.

'No,' replied the first, looking at the robe. 'It'd be a shame to tear
it. It's a good bit of stuff, this. Belonged to this Jesus fellow.'

'What, the King of the Jews?' was the comment. 'Here—who
wants a royal robe?'

There was a roar of laughter. Then one suggested that they
should tear it up the seams, and so divide it.

'There's no seam,' said the first soldier. 'It's woven in one piece.
I tell you what, let's throw dice for it. Who throws the highest gets
the robe.'

'That's fair enough. Got the dice?'

The dice were produced, shaken and thrown.

'A two,' said the soldier disgustedly, as he passed on the dice. 'No
kingly robe for me!'

The next man threw a five, the next four, and the last a six. 'To-
day's my lucky day,' he said. 'Hand it over,' and they gave him
Jesus' robe.

Above their heads the three prisoners hung in the scorching sun.
Presently one of them spoke.

'Hey you, King of the Jews!' His voice was weak and cracked,
but there was bitter scorn in his words. 'Where's your magic now?
Why don't you use it to get us off these crosses, eh?'

'Be quiet.' It was the voice of the other thief. 'We got what we deserved. But this man, he did nothing wrong.' And then he too turned his head towards Jesus and his words came in gasps for he was in great pain. 'Jesus, remember me when you come into your Kingdom.'

On the cross between the two thieves Jesus hung, and in spite of his agony, a look of compassion came to his face as he heard these unexpected words of faith. 'Friend,' he said, 'I tell you truly. To-day you shall be with me in Paradise.'

The crowd, growing weary of waiting, were deep in argument once more. Some protested that Jesus was the Christ, the King of Israel, to which a priest, with sarcastic authority, suggested that if that were so, perhaps Jesus would come down from the cross so that they might see and believe.

'Now's your chance, Messiah,' called a man. 'Come down off the cross!' And another mocked that he had saved others, but could not save himself. The priest took this opportunity to add that this was the man who had said he could destroy the temple and build it again in three days.

'You, that can build the temple in three days,' cried a voice from the crowd, 'save yourself and come down from the cross.'

'No, he can't save himself,' another said.

'Then let God save him,' said the priest. 'He trusts God. Let him deliver him now if he wants to, for he called himself the Son of God.'

'A blasphemer,' said another voice, trying to curry favour with the priests. 'Taking the name of the Lord God in vain—Son of Satan!'

Mary heard all these cries as she stood there, but she did not heed them. Her thoughts were with Jesus, in his agony. Presently she murmured to John, 'Let us go closer, John. I want him to know I am here.'

'You'll not be able to bear his agony, Mother Mary,' said John. But she answered, 'I must be near my son.'

So with Mary Magdalene, they moved nearer to the cross, but a soldier intercepted them, 'No closer, please. We've got our work to do.'

'We are friends of Jesus of Nazareth,' said John. 'This is his mother.'

The Roman soldier was shocked. For a moment he could not speak. Then he said with a rough kindness, 'This is no place for you, lady. There's nothing you can do for him. You'd much better go home.' He turned to John. 'Got someone at home, has she?' John shook his head.

Then Jesus spoke from the cross. 'Mother.'

She stepped nearer, her eyes looking up to where he hung above her. 'My son . . . ?'

'Take John for your son now—John—'

'Master?'

'She is your mother.'

'Yes, master,' said John, putting a protective arm around Mary.

There was silence for a moment as they stood looking up at the cross. Then Mary Magdalene gave a low cry. 'He is going. He is dying, John—our master is dying. The light of the world is leaving it.'

The darkness came down with terrifying suddenness. At one moment it was hot sunshine; the next, it was dark as night.

The people began to cry out in fear, some saying it was God's judgment, some that it was the power of Satan. And above the other cries came a woman's scream, 'God is leaving us!'

And there was darkness over all the land until the ninth hour, and at the ninth hour, Jesus cried with a loud voice—'My God, my God, why hast Thou forsaken me?'

When the light returned and Mary could again see her son's face, he looked at peace. His lips moved and she stepped nearer to hear the words.

'I thirst.'

Quickly she turned to Mary Magdalene. 'He's thirsty, Mary, have you the vinegar and water?'

'Yes, and a sponge I brought to bathe his brow.'

'Dip the sponge in it, lady,' said one of the soldiers kindly. 'And I'll hold it up to him on my spear.'

They watched with some anxiety while he attempted this, and the spear was just long enough for the sponge to reach Jesus' lips.

'He's taking it,' said his mother, with relief. 'He's lifting his head.'

Jesus lifted his head, and now his voice was strong and triumphant as he cried, 'It is finished!' Then, as softly he repeated a familiar boyhood prayer, 'Father, into Thy hands I commend my spirit,' he bowed his head again and yielded up his spirit.

The silence was broken by the Roman centurion. 'Truly,' he murmured, 'this man was the Son of God.'

They took the body of Jesus from the cross and wrapped it in linen and a man named Joseph of Arimathæa, who was a secret follower of Jesus, laid the body in his own new tomb which was in a garden close by the place of crucifixion. And they rolled a great stone against the door of the tomb and departed, for it was the Sabbath day.

Pilate was staring from his window towards the hill on which stood the three empty crosses. Outside the streets were quiet, for it was the Sabbath and few were abroad. He was disturbed by a centurion who told him that some members of the Sanhedrin were waiting to see him.

'Am I to have no peace from these accursed Jews?' asked Pilate angrily. 'What do they want now?'

'I think,' said the centurion gently, 'it is about the tomb of Jesus.'

Pilate looked at him. He too had been thinking of Jesus, dead in the tomb. The centurion went on to say that the priests complained that no guard had been set.

'I have washed my hands of Jesus,' said Pilate curtly. 'I will hear no more about it. By their desire he was crucified, and at their request the body was delivered to them.'

'Sir, with respect,' said the centurion, 'I think you should see them. They are powerful men, and will not take kindly to a message from me.'

Pilate sighed wearily. 'Very well,' he said, 'bring them in.'

The centurion went out and after another long look at the three crosses, Pilate walked to his seat and sat down. The centurion returned with Caiaphas, two priests and two Pharisees.

'Well, my lord Caiaphas,' said Pilate, 'what brings you here on the Sabbath day? I thought it was your day of rest.'

'Only a matter of the most extreme urgency would cause me to come on the Sabbath, your Excellency,' said Caiaphas. 'It has only to-day come to my ears that the man Jesus was buried in a private sepulchre.'

Pilate answered him sharply that this was at the request of one of their members.

'But without my knowledge, sir,' returned Caiaphas. 'That in itself is a serious matter, and one that shall be dealt with by the council. Joseph of Arimathæa will be charged and have to answer for his action. But my complaint to your Excellency is that the tomb has been left unguarded.'

With a touch of malice Pilate asked him, 'What are you afraid of now? By your will Jesus is crucified—dead and buried. Can you not let him rest in his grave?'

'No,' answered Caiaphas. 'It would not be safe.'

Pilate was at once uneasy. 'What do you mean?'

'Sir,' explained Caiaphas, 'while this impostor lived, he prophesied that three days after his death he would come back to life.'

Pilate rose to his feet, disturbed at this fresh suggestion of the supernatural.

'Don't you see what we are afraid of?' asked Caiaphas.

'That he will come out of his grave?'

'No, no, no,' said Caiaphas vehemently, 'but that his disciples may come and steal the body and say to the people, "He is risen." If they do this matters will be worse than they were before. The tomb must be sealed until the third day and guards set.'

'Get your own guards.'

'The body is Roman property, your Excellency.'

'No longer,' said Pilate. 'It was given into Jewish hands, and Jews must guard it.'

'But it is the Sabbath,' wailed Caiaphas.

'That is your business,' said Pilate firmly. 'If you want guards you must see to it yourselves, and make the grave secure as best you can.' He turned his back on them, and looked out of the window again, while Caiaphas and the priests, after an angry look at him, went out and left him. Though they broke their own laws by doing it, they had themselves to make arrangements for securing the tomb, sealing the stone and setting a guard over it.

That night, as the Sabbath ended, the earth trembled and shook. A great storm arose. Thunder crashed, and vivid flashes of lightning lit the sky. The guards watching the tomb were terrified.

Next morning the air was clear, and all signs of the tempest were gone, when Mary Magdalene, Salome the mother of James and John, and Mary Cleopas came to the garden very early, carrying baskets of herbs and spices to anoint the body of Jesus.

'How quiet it is,' said Mary Magdalene.

'Yes,' said Salome, 'and there's no sign of the earthquake that shook the city. Is this the right path?'

'Yes,' answered Mary, 'I remember the thorn bush here.' She stifled a sob as she remembered the face beneath the crown of thorns, and added quickly, 'See, it's breaking into bud.'

Salome saw her distress, and covered it with a homely platitude: 'Yes, even in the midst of death, new life begins.'

Mary smiled at her, then called out to Mary Cleopas to guide her to the right path, and added to Salome, 'I'm glad his mother didn't come. I don't think she could have borne it.'

Salome replied that her John would take care of Mary as he had promised, and that they would help each other through these first dark days. They waited for a moment for Mary Cleopas to come up to them. She was about forty, a sensitive, clever woman.

'It's so quiet,' she said, 'I could hear your voices from the other path. Look, I picked some wild anemones. He was fond of them. I hope the gardeners won't mind.'

'The gardeners aren't at work yet,' said Salome. 'It's good we came early. I'd sooner we were alone here with the master.'

But Mary said they could not be sure they would be alone, for there had been some talk the night before of a guard being set. Anyway, she said, looking round, there seemed to be no one about.

'Nobody about!' echoed Salome, with dismay. 'We've forgotten that great stone at the door of the tomb. It took four men to put it in place—who will roll it away for us?'

The two older women felt defeated and blamed themselves for not bringing Peter and John with them. Now they would have to wait for one of the gardeners to help—unless perhaps there *were* guards at the tomb who could be asked.

'They'd never do it,' said Mary Magdalene with conviction. 'They'd never let us near. Perhaps we can manage to move it. There are three of us, and we're strong. Let's try. It's just along here.'

They hurried along the path, but when they reached the tomb where they had laid the body of Jesus they stopped, bewildered and frightened, for the entrance to it was wide open, the great flat stone which formed the door having been rolled to one side.

'Someone has been here before us,' said Mary Cleopas at last.

'The guards,' whispered Mary Magdalene in horror. 'They've taken him! They've taken him away!'

Clinging to each other they moved nearer to the tomb, peering into its dark interior. Suddenly Mary Cleopas stopped them. 'Don't go any farther,' she said. 'There's something strange here.'

'I'm going to fetch John and Peter,' said Mary Magdalene, and, leaving the others in the garden, she ran back through the silent early morning streets to the house where the disciples lodged.

It was in the same upper room where they had eaten their last supper with Jesus that his unhappy disciples now hid. The doors were barred and on this morning they sat in dejected, frightened groups, discussing what they should do next. James thought they might as well go back to Galilee, and Andrew agreed that the sooner they got out of the city the better.

'Father'll be glad to have us,' said James to John. 'He's been on his own a long time now—mother away too.'

'Where is the lord's mother? Did she go to the tomb with your mother and Mary?' asked Andrew.

'No,' replied John. 'Her cousin went instead. She's resting now. How's Peter?'

Andrew pointed to where Peter sat apart from them, his head in his hands, then rose and went over to him and put an arm around his shoulder and said, 'Brother.'

Peter looked up, his face haunted. He spoke almost like a child.

'I didn't mean to. I didn't mean to, Andrew.'

'No,' said Andrew soothingly as though he was the father instead of the younger brother. 'Of course you didn't.'

'They asked me so suddenly,' went on Peter. 'I didn't know what

The Crucifixion

The empty tomb

Cleopas telling how he saw the master

I was saying . . . If we'd all been together I'd not have done it—or if the master had been there. It seems when he's not with me I've no courage.'

'It will come back, brother,' Andrew reassured him.

But Peter was still haunted by his thoughts. 'I'll never forget,' he said, 'the look he gave me as the cock crew. Till I die I'll see him as they led him away to be crucified. Never to see his face again. I've had my last chance to be Peter the Rock.'

Suddenly they heard footsteps running down the street, then up the stairs, and an urgent knocking at the door. The men sprang to their feet and spoke in whispers.

'The guards!' 'The police!' 'They've come to arrest us.' But Peter hoped it might be true. 'I'm ready,' he said.

Andrew went to the door and unbarred it. Mary Magdalene burst in. Breathlessly she called, 'John, Peter, come quickly—to the garden.'

'What is it?' asked Peter, alert now.

'He is gone!' said Mary. 'They have taken away the lord out of the tomb, and we don't know where they have laid him.'

The disciples looked at one another for a moment, frozen with amazement, questioning one another with their eyes. Then John made a move towards the door. 'James,' he ordered, 'stay with Mother Mary. Peter, come with me.'

They were off down the stairs in a moment, followed by Mary who could scarcely keep up with them as they raced along the streets towards the garden.

In the garden Salome paced restlessly up and down while Mary Cleopas sat rapt in thought. Presently she spoke.

'Salome, where did he go?'

'The master?' asked Salome.

'No,' said Mary. 'That young man who spoke to us. Where did he come from and where did he go? Who was he?'

'One of the gardeners, I suppose,' said the practical Salome.

'No,' said Mary, 'he wasn't a gardener. He spoke so strangely—' She broke off as she heard the sound of running feet, and a moment later John's voice saying, 'Past the thorn bush. This is the way. This way, Peter.' And John ran breathlessly up to them, followed very soon by Peter, and last by Mary Magdalene.

'Oh, John,' cried Salome, 'thank God you've come. See the stone, rolled away, and the tomb empty.'

'Are you sure it is empty?' asked John.

'Yes,' said Salome. 'After Mary went we looked and there was a young man there, and he showed us the place where the master lay.'

John and Peter went to the entrance of the tomb and looked in. Then John spoke urgently to Salome, asking who the man was, and what he had said. Salome told him that it was a young man in white, sitting in the tomb; and they had been terrified at the sight of him.

'He wasn't there when we looked before,' broke in Mary Magdalene.

'I don't know when he came or where from,' said Salome. 'I was so afraid, I hardly made out what he was saying. But he spoke kindly. I think he said if we were looking for Jesus of Nazareth he was not here but had been taken away.'

'No,' Mary Cleopas spoke firmly. 'He didn't say that. He said, "You have come to look for Jesus of Nazareth who was crucified. He has risen."'

They stared at her in amazement, only John repeating in a whisper, 'Risen?'

'And then he said,' went on Mary in the same firm voice, ' "Tell Peter and the other disciples that he is going before you into Galilee. There you shall see him as he promised you."'

Peter pushed the others aside, saying roughly, 'What does it mean? Who is playing tricks on us?'

He went into the tomb, but John stood where he was, saying almost to himself, ' "After I am risen, I will go on before you into Galilee." He *did* say that.' He was roused by Peter, calling urgently from the tomb.

'John, John, come here!' John ran to the tomb—Peter's voice was puzzled. 'The linen shroud that wrapped the body is still there—and the napkin that covered his head.'

John stepped through the entrance to the tomb while Peter went on, as if trying to sort out his own confused thoughts. 'I can understand the stone being moved. There was an earthquake tremor in the night, and that could have done it; but if it was that, who stole the body? And if stolen, why stripped and the grave-clothes left?'

'Not only left, but undisturbed,' said John.

'What?' cried Peter.

John spoke now with an undercurrent of growing excitement. 'Look! See how the shroud is folded exactly as though it still covered the body, and the napkin folded where his head lay.'

'But why?' demanded Peter. 'Who has done it? What does it mean?'

'I wonder, I wonder,' said John, as if to himself. 'Oh, master!' Then to Peter, 'That man the women saw, a man in white, could it have been an angel?'

'Don't go imagining things, John.' Peter's voice was harsh. 'The women were beside themselves. We don't know that they saw any-thing—man or angel, or anything else. All we know is the master's gone.'

'Risen?' queried John, memory coming to him. '"After three days I shall rise again"—it *is* the third day, Peter.'

But Peter could not bear this. 'Don't start remembering the things he said,' he begged. 'He's gone—that's all we know, and we must tell the others that and nothing else.'

They left the cave and went back to the women, and then set out on their way back to the town.

But Mary Magdalene stayed in the garden, and when the others had gone she sank down on her knees, covering her face with her hands and weeping bitterly, 'Master! Master! Where are you?'

But Mary was not alone in the garden. All at once she heard a voice behind her saying,

'Woman, why are you weeping? Whom do you seek?'

Mary, supposing it to be the man the other women had spoken of, or else one of the gardeners, answered, 'Because they have taken away my lord, and I don't know where they have taken him. Oh, sir, if you are one of the gardeners here perhaps you know where he is. Tell me where you have laid him, and I will take him away.' And she buried her head and began to cry again.

'Mary,' said Jesus quietly.

She looked up with a cry of incredulous joy and her hands reached out to him.

Gently, he said, 'Do not cling to me, for I have not yet gone up to the Father; but go to my brothers and tell them this. I am going back to Him who is my Father and your Father, and my God and your God.'

Then he left her, and Mary Magdalene, her heart filled with great joy, went to the disciples and told them that she had seen the lord and that he had said these things to her.

That same evening of the first day of the week the disciples were gathered together in Jerusalem in the upper room.

The table was laid for supper, but before they sat down to it they were talking together of all that had been told them.

'I think we are all here,' said James. 'Better lock the door, Andrew.'

Andrew counted. 'Seven, eight, nine—only nine. There should be twelve,' he said.

'No, not now,' James reminded him, 'only eleven,' and Andrew bit his lip at having brought back to memory the traitor Judas. But James went on to say that Thomas was missing—he hoped he was safe at Bethany with Martha and Lazarus. Nathaniel, he said, had gone to Emmaus with Cleopas and his wife.

Andrew locked the door, then turned back to James, asking what he made of the news, and that Peter believed that the lord had risen. James told him that John too believed it. 'But what have we to go on? An empty tomb and the story of a frightened girl.'

'That's what Peter said at first,' replied Andrew. 'But something's happened to change him. You know how he's been these two days—half dead with grief and remorse—well, look at him to-night!'

They looked at Peter, who was sitting at the table with John beside him. There was confidence now in his manner, a joy in his face, as he listened to John, who was speaking to Philip and Matthew, telling them that it must be true, and that Jesus had said to Mary: 'Tell my brothers I am going back to my Father and your Father and my God and your God.'

'It was a vision,' said Matthew.

'But what about that message the other woman brought—something about going back to Galilee?' said James, and Andrew joined in saying he thought they should now go back there, and that was where the master would want them to be.

But Matthew, practical as ever, demurred. 'Not yet,' he said.

There's this mystery of the empty tomb to clear up. If they stole
he body of our lord, we've got to find him.'

'He has found us,' said Peter, quiet and radiant.

'But, Peter,' argued Andrew, 'I know Mary says that she has seen
im and she believes it, but it was a vision, not our lord himself.'

'It was no vision,' said Peter quietly.

'Why, Peter,' asked John, 'have you seen him?'

'I thought my last memory of him would be as a prisoner being
ed away as the cock crew. But I have seen him—free, strong, and
orgiving.'

The disciples gathered round him in amazement, but at that moment there was a sudden loud knocking at the door. As usual, their
irst thought was that it might be the police, but they knew too that
t might be Thomas, so John called through the door to ask who
it was.

'Nathaniel and Cleopas,' came the answer. He unlocked the
door, and let them in. They were in a state of great excitement.

'We have seen him!' cried Nathaniel. 'We have seen the master!'

The other disciples surged round them. Their questions tumbled
out in their wild hope and excitement.

'It was on the road to Emmaus,' began Cleopas. 'We were going
back to our village and talking together about—about what had
happened, and we didn't notice at first that a man was walking beside us, listening to what we said.'

'Who was it?' asked James eagerly.

'We didn't know then.'

'Did he speak to you?' questioned Andrew.

'Yes,' said Nathaniel. 'He asked us what we were talking about
and why we seemed so sad.'

Cleopas took up the tale again. ' "Are you a stranger in Jerusalem," I said, "that you do not know the things that have happened
there these last days?" And he said, "What things?" "Why, about
Jesus of Nazareth." I said. "The great prophet of God, who did
such mighty works. Have you not heard how he was condemned to
death and crucified? We had hoped he was to redeem Israel,"
I said, "but now all that is past and the third day is passing too." '

'And then what happened?' asked John.

'What happened then, Nathaniel?' asked Cleopas, and Nathaniel prompted him. 'You told him about the empty tomb—and the angel.'

'Oh, yes,' said Cleopas, taking up the tale again. 'I said that some of the women who had followed Jesus, my wife among them, went to his grave early this morning and found the body gone, and had astonished us by saying that they had seen an angel at the tomb who told them Jesus was alive.'

'Yes, yes,' interrupted John, scarcely able to wait, 'but what did *he* say?'

'He didn't say anything to that,' replied Cleopas. 'I went on to tell him how some of you had gone to the tomb and found it empty, as the women had said, but that nobody had seen the angel.'

'That was when he began to talk to us,' added Nathaniel, and John asked eagerly what he had said.

'He said, "Was it not to be expected that the Messiah would suffer before coming into his glory?" And then, walking along the road beside us he reminded us of all the things that had been written in the scriptures about the Messiah. It warmed our hearts to hear him.'

'All the way to the village he talked to us,' said Cleopas. 'And when we reached our house it was getting dark, and I asked him if he would come in and stay with us.'

'And did he?' questioned John.

'Yes, he did. My wife prepared a meal and he sat down with us, and for some reason I asked him to bless the bread.'

'It was as he broke the bread that we recognized him,' Nathaniel broke in. 'Not only because of the wounds on his hands, but there was something familiar about the way he did it and the way he said the grace. It was as though we'd been blind before and suddenly our eyes were opened like those poor blind ones he healed.'

'But where is he now?' asked John.

'Who knows?' replied Cleopas. 'Directly after he broke the bread he disappeared.'

'Disappeared!' echoed Matthew, loud in his disappointment. 'Then it was only a vision after all!'

Some of the other disciples began to murmur among themselves, but Nathaniel spoke firmly.

'It was no vision. He was flesh and blood, like you and me.'

'Peace be unto you'

'I am with you always'

'But why did he disappear?' protested Matthew. 'Why didn't he come back here with you? Why haven't any of us seen him?'

'Peter has seen him,' broke in John. 'Peter and Mary and these two here.'

'I still say they all saw a vision.'

'No, no, flesh and blood.'

'It doesn't seem possible.'

'With God all things are possible.'

And suddenly, as they argued among themselves, they heard a familiar voice.

'Peace be unto you.'

The disciples had been gathered at one end of the table. Now they swung round in amazement and some cried out in joy and some in terror at what they saw. For standing in front of the locked door, and smiling a little at their bewilderment, was Jesus. Nobody moved, then Jesus spoke again.

'It is I, do not be afraid. Why do you wonder in your hearts? Can you not see that it is I? Look at my hands and feet—touch me. You see—a spirit has not flesh and bones, has it?'

Peter and John were the first to move—they ran to him and John took one of the wounded hands and held it to his face. Then with wonder and exclamations of joy, the others crowded round, some coming to touch Jesus, others falling on their knees.

Jesus asked them if they had anything to eat.

'Yes, master,' said Andrew. 'There is bread and fish and a honey-comb.' Jesus sat at the table, and they waited on him as he ate some of the fish and the honey. Matthew was almost crying with happiness.

'I can't believe it, I can't believe it,' he said again and again. 'The master sitting at supper with us, just like . . . just like he always did. Master, you'll stay with us now, won't you?' he asked hesitatingly, voicing the thoughts of them all.

'I am with you always,' replied Jesus, 'even though I return to the Father—even though you will not see me.'

At this all the disciples protested, begging him to stay with them and not to go away, for they needed him, but he quietened them. 'Peace,' he said gently. 'Peace, my children. Did I not tell you when I walked with you that the Christ must suffer and be put to death and on the third day rise again? And after this return to God our Father? So was it prophesied and so must it be. For I was sent here to do my Father's will. And as He sent me so now do I send you to teach men of all nations the gospel of repentance and forgiveness of sins in the name of Christ.' They looked with rapt faces as he added, 'Receive now the gift of the Holy Spirit that was promised you by my Father. . . .'

There was silence in the room, broken at last by Matthew.

'He has gone,' he said; but now they were no longer terrified by what had happened nor by any fear of the supernatural. They were calm and happy.

'We are not alone any more,' said Nathaniel. 'We'll never feel alone any more.' And the others agreed that Jesus was closer than ever to them now, because he had brought them nearer to the Father—'the ladder between earth and heaven,' as Nathaniel put it.

Only Peter was moved too deeply for words, and he sat for a while staring at the empty place beside him, where Jesus had sat. Then he rose and led the others in the prayer that Jesus had taught them.

'Our Father who art in Heaven, hallowed be Thy name. Thy Kingdom come. Thy will be done on earth as it is in Heaven. Give us this day our daily bread, and forgive us our debts as we forgive our debtors. Lead us not into temptation but deliver us from evil, for Thine is the Kingdom, the power and the glory, for ever,' and Peter added the words, 'through Jesus Christ, our Lord,' 'Amen.'

Eight days later the disciples were again gathered together in the upper room, and this time Thomas Didymus was with them. Over and over again the other men had described to him how Jesus had appeared to them, but Thomas was unconvinced. Now he sat with his head in his hands, the only desolate one in that cheerful company.

'I don't believe it, I just *can't* believe it,' he muttered.

'It's true, Thomas,' said Peter who sat beside him. 'He sat where you are sitting now. He ate with us and we saw the marks of the nails in his hands.'

'It was a vision—or a spirit.'

'Has a vision flesh and bones?' asked Peter. 'I tell you we touched him. We held his hands.'

Thomas shook his head. 'It's beyond reason that the dead should come alive.'

'Jesus *is* alive, Thomas.'

But Thomas could not believe. 'I tell you,' he cried, 'unless *I* see in his hands the print of the nails and can put my fingers in the wounds, I will not believe it,' and he bowed his face in his hands again.

'Peace be unto you.'

The disciples swung round, this time without fear. Thomas raised his head in bewilderment and followed the gaze of the other disciples. There, in front of the locked door, stood Jesus.

'Thomas.' Thomas rose to his feet but could not speak. Jesus held out his hands to him. 'Come, Thomas, come and feel my hands.'

Slowly, his eyes fixed on the familiar face, Thomas walked towards Jesus. When he stood before him, Jesus said quietly: 'Do not be faithless, but believe.'

Thomas no longer needed to touch his master in order to believe. Falling on his knees, he called out: 'My lord and my God!'

Jesus spoke to him gently. 'Because you have seen me you have believed. Blessed are those who have not seen me and yet believe.'

Soon after this the disciples returned to Galilee.

One evening when the four fishermen went out on the lake in Simon Peter's boat they took Philip, Nathaniel and Thomas with them. But although they fished all night they caught nothing.

'Empty again,' said Peter as he and James hauled in the net.

'Dawn's breaking,' said James. 'Shall we put about and make for home?'

'Yes,' agreed Peter, and he turned to Thomas and the others. 'Sorry, lads, I wanted to show you a good night's fishing on the lake. But either the wind or the weather is against us.'

'Or you've been away from it so long you've lost your touch,' chaffed Thomas, and the others joined in the laughter.

'Turn her about, John,' said James. John stood in the stern holding the tiller, but instead of turning the boat he pointed towards the shore.

'There's a man standing on the shore,' he said. 'Seems to have a fire.' They all turned and across the water the man called to them.

'Have you lads caught any fish?'

'No, nothing,' called Peter.

'Cast your net on the right side of the boat and you'll have a catch.'

'What does he say?' asked James.

'Says to cast on the right side,' said Peter. 'Probably been out himself and knows there's a shoal there. No harm in trying.'

With James' help he cast the net on the other side of the boat, while the others peered down into the water; all except John who still gazed towards the figure standing on the shore.

Presently there was a definite tug on the net and the boat listed over on the right side.

Peter called out anxiously: 'Not all on this side—trim the boat—hold her steady, John—Thomas and you, Nathaniel, over to the other side.'

'It's full,' said James in great excitement. 'The net's full to breaking—lend a hand, Andrew.'

'We'll never get it aboard,' said Andrew. 'Better tow it behind the boat.'

'As fine a haul as I've ever seen,' exulted Peter. 'That fellow was right. Haul away, lads.'

But John, still staring at the shore, spoke with a new excitement. 'Peter,' he said, 'it's the lord.'

Peter left the net to James and Andrew and he too looked towards the shore, and now his face lit with joy. 'Hold fast to the net, lads,' he said. 'I'm taking her into shore.'

They headed for the shore, impeded by the heavy net, and Peter, impatient of delay, pushed past the others, jumped overboard and swam to the beach, where Jesus stood by a fire, awaiting him with a smile. Peter waded ashore, shook the water from his eyes, and stood there looking, unable to speak.

He glanced down at the little fire on which some fishes were cooking, then up at his master's face. 'Bring some of the fish you have just caught,' said Jesus.

The boat drew into the side of the lake and ground on the shingle. The disciples leapt from it, and ran forward to greet Jesus.

This time there was no fear, but only intense joy at this happy surprise.

'Haul the net into shore, lads,' said Peter. 'Careful it doesn't break with the weight.'

'More than a hundred, I'd say,' said James. 'Big ones too.'

'Pick out a dozen to take to the fire,' said Peter. 'We're going to have breakfast here.'

John and James busied themselves with counting the fish, while others helped with the cooking of those they set aside for the meal.

Then they gathered round Jesus, who took some bread and broke it, saying the familiar blessing, 'Blessed be Thou, O Lord our God, King of the World, who bringeth forth bread from the earth.' Then he gave a piece to each disciple, with some fish.

They ate their meal peacefully and happily together, and then, while the others stretched out the nets to dry Jesus spoke to Simon Peter.

'Simon, Son of Jonah, do you love me more than these others do?'

'Lord,' said Peter humbly, remembering his boast that though all should forsake Jesus, he would not, 'lord, you know that I love you.'

'Then feed my lambs,' said Jesus, and the hope began to dawn on Peter that he was, after all, the Rock, that in spite of his denial he was to be trusted. Jesus asked him again, 'Simon, do you indeed love me?'

'Why, lord,' answered Peter in surprise, 'you know that I love you.'

'Then be a shepherd to my sheep,' said Jesus, and as Peter nodded in agreement, he asked him yet again, 'Simon, are you my friend?'

Simon was troubled at the question being put for the third time. The word 'friend' reminded him of Jesus' words at the last supper, 'The greatest love that a man can show is to lay down his life for his friend.' Could he claim to be Jesus' friend, he wondered.

'Your friend?' he repeated. 'Lord, you know all things, what is past and what is to come. Look into my heart and know that I love you.'

'Feed my flock,' said Jesus, and Peter nodded again. 'Indeed I say to you, Peter, when you were young you dressed yourself and went whichever way you chose. But when you have grown old you will stretch out your hands for someone else to gird you, and you will be taken to a place not of your choosing.'

'The way you went, lord?' asked Peter, realizing that Jesus was speaking of his crucifixion.

'Follow me,' said Jesus, and Peter answered, 'Lord, I will follow you.'

The other disciples came back to the fire and as they sat in a circle around it Jesus told them of their mission.

'You are my witnesses,' he said, 'and that the world may know that I have been given power in Heaven and on earth, you must go and teach all nations the things that you have seen and heard, baptizing them in the name of the Father and of the Son and of the Holy Spirit. And know that I am with you always—even unto the end of the world.'

And there are also many other things which Jesus did, the which, if they should be written every one, I suppose that even the world itself could not contain the books that should be written.—JOHN, XXI, 25